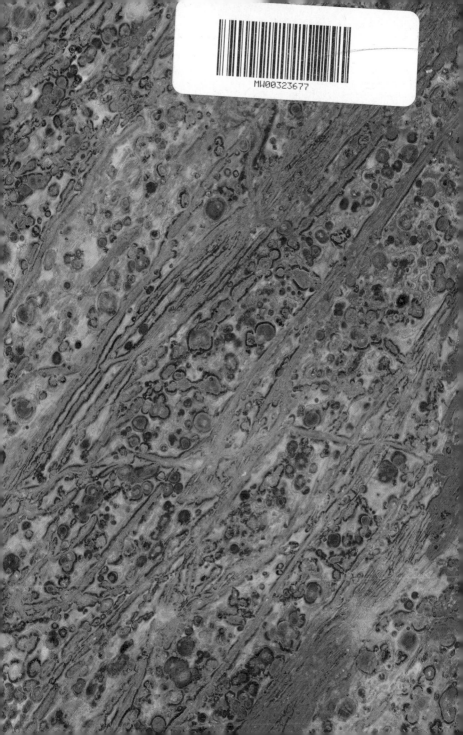

WORLD of GEMSTONES

by Rudolf Ďuďa and Luboš Rejl

GEOSCIENCE PRESS, Inc.
Tucson, Arizona

English translation published by Geoscience Press, Inc.,
P. O. Box 42948, Tucson, AZ 85733–2948
© 1998 by Geoscience Press, Inc.
Library of Congress Card Catalog Number: 98–4830
ISBN 0–945005–30–X

First published in Czech Republic under the title SVĚT DRAHÝCH KAMENŮ
by Granit Publishing House, Prague
© 1996 RNDr. Rudolf Ďuďa and RNDr. Luboš Rejl

© 1996 Photographs by Jeff Scovil (85), Jiří Bursík (56), Dušan Slivka (12), František Tvrz (10), Karel Mařík (6),
Karel Valter (4), Zdeněk Prokopec (1), Petr Korbel (1), and photobank Granit.

We thank all of the private collectors and institutions who gave permission
to publish pictures of their specimens.

End–papers: Leopard jasper, Mexico
Page 2: Elbaite crystal on quartz, 32 mm long, Minas Gerais, Brazil.
Page 3: Slices of elbaite crystals (so called watermelon tourmalines), Brazil.
Page 4: Moss agate, Doubravice near Jičín, Czech Republic.
Page 6: Agate with amethyst, Horní Halže, Czech Republic.
Page 7: Malachite (cut), Ural Mts., Russia.
Page 22: Various tumbled gemstones.

Printed in Czech Republic

Library of Congress Cataloging–in–Publication Data

Ďuďa, Rudolf. (Svět drahých kamenů, English)
World of gemstones / by Rudolf Ďuďa and Luboš Rejl; translated by Petr Korbel.
p. cm.
Includes bibliographical references (p. 188) and index.
ISBN 0–945005–30–X
1. Precious stones. I. Rejl, Luboš. II. Title.
QE392.D8313 1998
553.8—dc21 98–4830
CIP
10/01/03/01

Contents

The world can be reflected in different ways,
in a gemstone it mirrors itself.

Zarathushtra

The book you have just opened is intended not only for gemstone experts – gemologists, mineralogists, jewelers, collectors, and dealers – but also for the general public, who come into contact with gemstones only occasionally, in jewelry, on display, or in various publications. It is divided into three parts. The introductory part provides basic information about gemstones and their properties, as well as how to identify, process, and take care of them. It explains chemical and physical terms, host rocks and occurrences, treatment, different ways of processing, and problems with the care of gemstones; it also touches on their healing effects. Supplied with useful illustrations, the main part of the book serves as a monograph on gemstones. Particular properties are grouped together so that readers can identify gemstones directly, either by visual observation or with simple laboratory tests. The final part includes additional information, a list of recommended reading, and an index.

Definition of the term
gemstone

Stones having an extraordinary look, luster, color, transparency, durability, or rarity – and meeting certain practical and commercial standards – were historically classified as gemstones. Later, often based on local importance, mystery, or fashion, other stones were also included, even though they lacked some of these properties. The trend continued until the experts divided gemstones into two groups: **precious** and **semiprecious** stones. As the number of gemstones increased and came to include unique stones as well as organic materials, the boundary line between precious and semiprecious stones blurred, so that today only a single group, **gemstones**, is officially recognized. *All minerals, rocks, or organic materials that can be cut for jewelry or collecting, or that can be used in their natural shape for making jewelry, mosaics, art or decorative objects,* are included. Unfortunately, this simplification has brought together extraordinary stones and very common ones, and has complicated the work of gemologists (especially commercial ones). With the growing number of people interested in gemstones, the use of improved identification techniques, and the recognition of more distinct features, new systems of classification have emerged. One system divides gemstones into classes (or groups) according to their use: jewelry, jewelry–decorative, decorative, and so on. Another, one of the best – and the system this book will use – divides them into **principal**, **important**, **common**, **rare**, and **synthetic** gemstones.

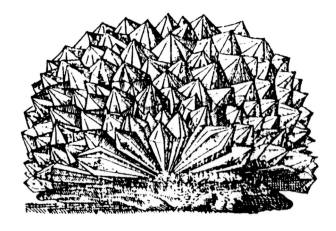

Names of gemstones, chemical formulas

Most of the older gemstones' names reflect their colors, shapes, or both, and are derived from Greek, Latin, Arabic, Turkish, German, Spanish, French, and certain Asian words (based mostly on where the gemstones were first discovered). Newer gemstones are named after localities or geographic features, famous people, organizations, and so on. Names and chemical formulas of gemstones in this book follow accepted international nomenclature and Fleischer and Mandarino, *Glossary of Mineral Species* (Tucson, 1995), respectively.

Visually observable properties

Color

Color belongs to the "very important" features visible to the naked eye that, often depending on fashion (at various times, red, green, purple, pink, blue) or on location (Arabia – blue stones; Central America – green stones), determine the value of a stone. Once the single most important commercial criterion for choosing a gemstone, color remains a "decisive feature." Some stones bear their typical color in their names (aquamarine, albite), while others have varied colors, which can prove difficult for identification. From the viewpoint of physics, we can divide gemstones into the following groups:

colorless (achromatic): light is not absorbed in the stone (diamond, rock crystal);

colored (idiochromatic): color is caused by the presence of certain constituent elements, which therefore appear in the chemical formula (malachite, rhodonite);

colored (allochromatic): color is caused by a trace amount of certain elements not specified in the chemical formula (amethyst, smoky quartz);

seemingly colored (pseudochromatic): color is caused by various optical effects: iridescence, chatoyancy, opalescence, aventurescence, labradorescence, dispersion, and pleochroism, as well as effects resulting from internal crystal structure (color zonation).

Diaphaneity (transparency)

This term describes the ability of a stone to transmit light. It is affected mainly by crystal grain size, inclusions, cracks, and so on. We can distinguish **transparent**, **semitransparent**, **translucent**, and **opaque** stones. Transparency can be reduced by irradiation, heating, and mechanical damage. The degree of transparency not only influences the quality and price of gemstones, but it is also a decisive factor in choosing how to process them (faceted cuts, cabochons, glyptics).

Luster

Luster is caused by the reflection and diffusion of light on or immediately below the surface of the observed face of a stone. It is determined by refractive index, absorption, diaphaneity, character of the face, and nature of the material. We can distinguish **metallic** (native gold), **submetallic** (cuprite), **adamantine** (diamond), **glassy** (sapphire), **greasy** (amber), **pearly** (feldspar), **silky** (tiger's-eye), and **dull** (turquoise) luster. One of the "important" properties of gemstones, luster has some influence on choosing how to cut or process a stone.

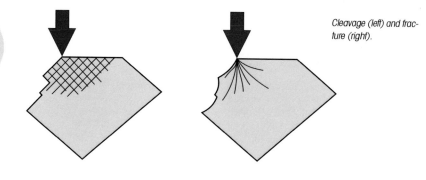

Cleavage (left) and fracture (right).

Cleavage

Cleavage is the tendency of a mineral to split in regular directions. It is always caused by the mineral's crystal structure and is always constant for each mineral species, as opposed to fissility, which is caused by the presence of twinning planes or the regular distribution of inclusions. We can distinguish **perfect** (topaz), **good** (andalusite), **indistinct** (emerald), or **poor** (tourmaline) cleavage. Knowing a gemstone's cleavage enables a stone cutter to make a good selection and orientation before cutting. Stones having perfect to good cleavage need to be protected from sudden shocks and sudden temperature changes.

Fracture

Fracture is the tendency of a mineral to break in *other* than regular directions. We can distinguish **conchoidal** (obsidian), **uneven** (kyanite), **splintery** (charoite), and **hackly** (native silver) fracture.

Crystal systems

Most natural gemstones occur as well–formed crystals. The symmetrical arrangement of atoms and molecules within a crystal – the crystal lattice – determines its external shape, as well as its optical and many of its physical properties. The angles between like external faces are constant for all crystals of a given mineral. There are only six basic ways that atoms and molecules can be symmetrically arranged to form crystals. The six crystal systems are called **triclinic**, **monoclinic**, **orthorhombic**, **tetragonal**, **hexagonal**, and **cubic** (isometric).

In distinguishing crystal systems, it is convenient to refer to three imaginary "axes" that cross in the center of an ideal crystal. The symmetry of a crystal system can then be described in terms of the relative lengths of the axes and the angles they form in the "axial cross."

The **triclinic** axes are unequal in length and form angles other than right angles with one another (axinite, kyanite). The **monoclinic** axes are also unequal in length, but two axes form right angles with one another (gypsum, orthoclase). The **orthorhombic** axes are unequal in length, but all three form right angles with one another (topaz, olivine). In the **tetragonal** system, two axes are equal in length, while a third axis of different length forms right angles with the other two (zircon, scapolite). In the **hexagonal** system, two axes are equal in length and form a 120_ angle, while a third axis of different length forms right angles with the other two (beryl, apatite). The **cubic** axes are all equal in length and all form right angles with one another (diamond, garnet).

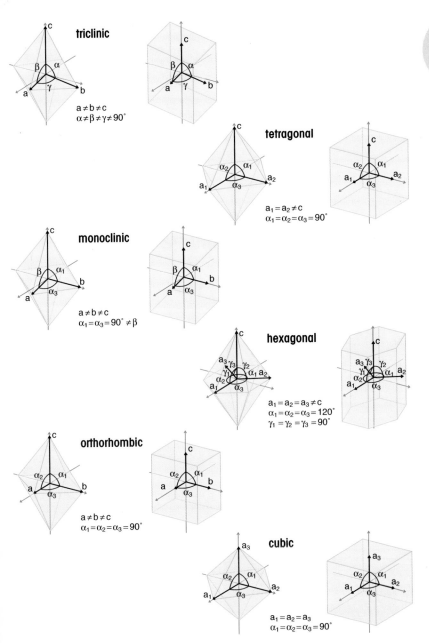

Examples of simple crystal shapes in six basic crystal systems, together with their parameters. Symmetry axes are boldface and axial crosses in blue to clearly show center of symmetry of each crystal system.

Morphology

Crystal structure and host rocks are the most important factors determining the morphology of a gemstone. Although, ideally, crystals are regularly developed, most of the time we deal with only imperfect individual crystals or their aggregates. Gemstones with no regular crystal structure are said to be amorphous (opal). According to external appearance (habit), we use different names for different shapes: **iso-metric** (diamond, garnet); **elongated in one direction** – columnar (tourmaline); **elongated in two directions** – platy (barite) or leafy (lepidolite); and **transitional** – barrel–like (sapphire). Other morphological features of gemstones include twinning and multiple intergrowth (staurolite crosses). Aggregates of gemstones used for jewelry may have a grainy, massive, fibrous, scaly, oolitic, dendritic, coloform, or filmy morphology.

Properties determined using simple instruments or tools

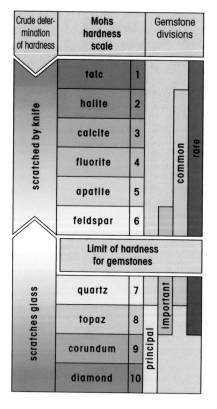

Crude determination of hardness	Mohs hardness scale		Gemstone divisions
scratched by knife	talc	1	
	halite	2	
	calcite	3	common / rare
	fluorite	4	
	apatite	5	
	feldspar	6	
	Limit of hardness for gemstones		
scratches glass	quartz	7	principal / important
	topaz	8	
	corundum	9	
	diamond	10	

Hardness

Hardness is the resistance of a gemstone to scratching. Of the several proportional hardness scales proposed, the best known is the Mohs scale. When testing the hardness of a stone, be careful not to damage facets, edges, and corners.

Streak

Rubbing a gemstone on an unglazed porcelain plate gives the color of its streak, which can be the same color as the stone (most idiochromatic stones) or completely different (pyrite's streak is black). Allochromatic stones usually have a white or very pale colored streak. Again, be careful not to damage facets, edges, and corners when determining a gemstone's streak.

Gemstones can be any hardness, but those with Mohs scale values below 6 are generally not suitable for ringstones.

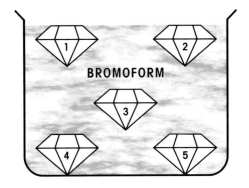

Specific gravity by suspension method
1 quartz
2 emerald
3 danburite
4 diamond
5 ruby

Specific gravity

The ratio of mass to volume in the metric system, specific gravity is one of the measurements used to identify a gemstone, since it varies only slightly among specimens of a particular gemstone. The suspension method is a relatively fast and accurate way to determine a stone's specific gravity. A stone is suspended in a liquid of known specific gravity. If it floats, its specific gravity is lower than the liquid's; if it sinks, its specific gravity is higher. With an appropriate range of heavy liquids, quite a variety of gemstones can be distinguished. To measure the specific gravity precisely, the double weighing method is used, with the stone weighed once in air and once in water.

Refractive index

When a light beam from an optically thinner environment (air) penetrates an optically denser environment (stone) at a specific angle – the angle of incidence – it refracts (bends). If the light beam is perpendicular to the given surface, there is no refraction. Refractive index is another important measurement used to identify gemstones.

Reflection and refraction of light. Optically denser environment is gray.

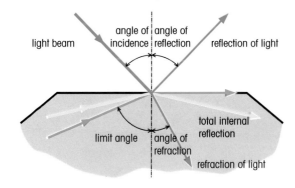

Birefringence

Gemstones with different optical properties in different directions refract light differently in those directions. Anisotropic stones will split a light beam into two different polarized beams, an effect called birefringence, which can be measured in the laboratory. Birefringence does not occur along the optical axes. Calcite and zircon exhibit a distinct birefringence, visible to the naked eye. Stone cutters need to consider birefringence when faceting.

Dispersion

Different wavelengths of light are refracted at different angles in gemstones, causing white light to split up into its component colors. This highly valued effect, called dispersion, is distinct in gemstones like diamond and zircon. Certain synthetic stones, imitating diamonds, also exhibit very high dispersion (cubic zirconia – CZ, YAG, and others).

Pleochroism

Some birefringent gemstones absorb light differently in different directions, so that different colors can be observed along and perpendicular to the optical axis. This effect is called pleochroism. Uniaxial stones such as tourmaline and beryl show two different colors (dichroism). Biaxial stones such as cordierite and kunzite show three different colors (trichroism). We can distinguish **strong, distinct**, and **weak** pleochroism. Although visible pleochroism is not present in most gemstones, it is possible to intensify or weaken pleochroism by careful orientation with respect to the optical axes when cutting.

Luminescence

Luminescence is the ability of certain gemstones to emit light from the transfer of different kinds of energy. When caused by UV light, this effect is called fluorescence if it lasts for only a short period of time, and phosphorescence if it lasts longer. An auxiliary identification feature, luminescence is brought about by trace amounts of certain elements, which may produce different colors of light in different gemstones. Because a gemstone may be luminescent from one locality and not from another, luminescence can help determine the exact locality of a particular stone.

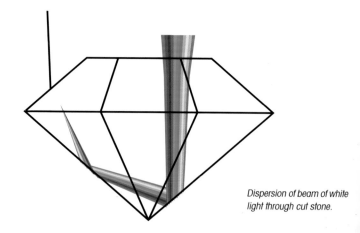

Dispersion of beam of white light through cut stone.

Treatment

Treatment is any process that aesthetically improves the look of a gemstone without significantly changing its chemical composition or physical properties. Gemstones are most often treated to intensify or weaken their color, or to retouch flaws (cracks, feathers, pores). Probably the best–known treatment is the dyeing of agates and chalcedony. Suitable porous specimens are impregnated with various pigments or dyes, by themselves or together with acids, lyes, or heating, to obtain the desired color. Heating can intensify color (aquamarine, sapphire), weaken it (morion, smoky quartz), or change it altogether (tourmaline, zircon). Irradiation can also intensify gemstone colors (diamond, aquamarine, kunzite, amethyst, smoky quartz, pearls). For partial reconstructions or retouches, gemstones are impregnated with various oils, resins, and other agents having refractive indices close to those of the stones treated. Some gemstones (turquoise, amber) can be reconstructed through thermal and pressure homogenization of fragments. Inclusions can be removed from diamonds by laser beam and the resulting channels filled with highly refractive glass.

History
of gemstones

We know from archaeological excavations that interest in gemstones dates back to Mesolithic times. Gemstones were mined and processed at a very high level in central and eastern Asia, Mesopotamia, Babylonia, Egypt, and Mesoamerica. Although we have documentary evidence that the ancient Greeks, Romans, and Byzantines were admirers of and experts in gemstones, only a few attempts to process gemstones and to use them in jewelry were made in central and northern Europe. Baltic amber was traded throughout the entire ancient world. Black bracelets made by Celtic tribes from a variety of coal found near what is today Nové Strašecí, Czech Republic, are another example of widely traded ancient jewelry.

Interest in gemstones rose significantly in Europe with progress in science and commerce during the 15th and 16th centuries. The association of gemstones with astrological signs and with beliefs in the supernatural also played a role. Interest peaked in the 18th and 19th centuries, when many new gemstone deposits were discovered and old deposits were rediscovered. At present, nontraditional gemstones and those with less than ideal properties are becoming more and more popular.

Astrology and gemstone healing

In addition to their aesthetic attributes, the often exceptional properties of gemstones caused them to be used as cult objects in prehistoric times. Later, astrologers associated gemstones with particular signs of the zodiac or with other stellar and planetary combinations. The unusual physical properties of particular stones, such as electric conductivity (quartz, tourmaline) or magnetism (hematite), led them to be used for healing (quartz and tourmaline for transferring energy; hematite for healing rheumatism). Healing with gemstones is done by apply-

Gemstones associated with signs of zodiac

Sign		Egyptians and Greeks	Byzantines	Jews	Medieval astrologers	Modern astrologers
🐏	21.3.–20.4.	amethyst	garnet	sapphire	sapphire diamond	garnet
🐂	21.4.–20.5.	obsidian	amethyst	chalcedony	emerald chrysoprase	amethyst
👫	21.5.–21.6.	heliotrope	jasper	emerald	pearls agate	aquamarine
🦀	22.6.–22.7.	chalcedony	diamond	onyx	ruby carnelian	diamond
🦁	23.7.–23.8.	emerald	emerald	carnelian	onyx sardonyx	emerald
♍	24.8.–23.9.	sardonyx	pearls	chrysolite	chrysolite	pearls
⚖	24.9.–23.10.	carnelian	ruby	aquamarine	aquamarine opal	ruby
♏	24.10.–22.11.	chrysolite	chrysolite	beryl topaz	topaz tiger's-eye	chrysolite
♐	23.11.–21.12.	beryl	sapphire	ruby	zircon turquoise	sapphire
♑	22.12.–20.1.	topaz	opal	garnet	garnet rose quartz	opal
♒	21.1.–19.2.	chrysoprase	topaz	amethyst	amethyst onyx	topaz
♓	20.2.–20.3.	hyacinth	turquoise	jasper	tourmaline jasper	turquoise

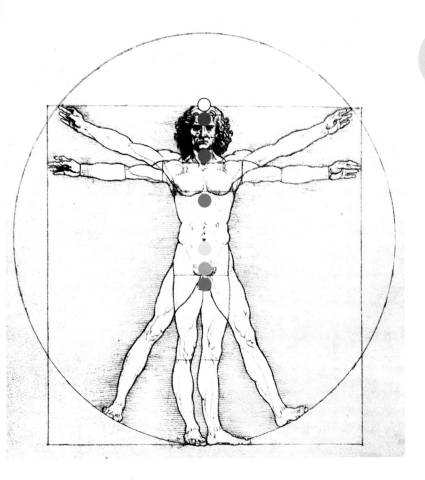

*Chakras (top to bottom): crown (white),
forehead (purple), throat (blue), heart (green),
navel (yellow), sacral (orange), base (red).*

ing them singly or in different combinations to painful places or to important nervous or energetic centers, such as chakras. Stones of a particular color are often used. Each stone actively used in healing needs to be discharged and then recharged from time to time. The stone is usually discharged in running water, then recharged in sunlight. Although the authors consulted many specialized books on the choice and application of healing stones, they did not verify any of the claims made in these sources. If you do not believe in the extraordinary power of gemstones, it does not matter. Go to any shop where gemstones are sold and find one that attracts you most by its shape, look, or color. If you wear and touch this stone often, you will create your own specific, indefinable relationship with it. You will recharge or discharge yourself through it. The stone will become a store of energy, a psychological support for you, which you will touch in all kinds of unusual situations.

Host rocks and occurrences

Gemstones occur in all basic rock types. While the largest known concentrations of gemstones are found in sedimentary rocks (diamonds, sapphires, rubies), a significant number are found in pegmatites. Originally, gemstones were collected on the surface; later, as new techniques developed and interest in gemstones grew, they were mined, with the volume often reaching incredible proportions (diamond mining in South Africa). Favorable conditions for the concentration of gemstones in any rock type are very rare and often accidental. In prospecting for gemstones, you therefore need to know certain rules (prospect only in geologically probable environments) – but you also need to be lucky. Otherwise, you may only be able to buy a gemstone. The gem business has its own special rules and tricks, so it is not unusual to get inaccurate information (sometimes vague, sometimes completely false) about where a given gemstone is located. For the same reason, information about the richness and accessibility of particular localities is also often inaccurate. Thus some of the illustrated gemstones in this book do not have an exact locality given.

Gemstones according to their more important host rocks – or their sources

Sedimentary rocks – about 50% of world gemstone production:
agate, alabaster, aragonite, calcite, chrysoberyl, diamond, garnets, gold, gypsum, jade, marcasite, monazite, platinum, quartz, rhodochrosite, ruby, sapphire, spinel

Pegmatites – about 15% of world gemstone production:
achroite, amazonite, andalusite, apatite, beryl, brazilianite, chrysoberyl, cordierite, corundum, eudialyte, feldspar, indicolite, kunzite, lepidolite, monazite, quartz, rubellite, schorl, spinel, spodumene, topaz, tourmaline, verdelite, zircon

Weathering zones – about 7% of world gemstone production:
azurite, chrysocolla, chrysoprase, cuprite, goethite, hematite, malachite, opal, smithsonite, turquoise, vivianite

Volcanic rocks:
agate, amethyst, apatite, chalcedony, citrine, jasper, nepheline, obsidian, olivine (peridot), opal, sapphire, silver

Igneous rocks:
bronzite, diamond, nepheline, platinum, pyrope, sapphire, titanite

Metamorphic and metasomatic rocks:
andalusite, beryl, charoite, chrysoberyl, cordierite, corundum, emerald, epidote, garnet, jadeite, jasper, kyanite, lazurite, nephrite, pyrite, rhodonite, scapolite, serpentine, sphalerite, spinel, staurolite, tiger's–eye, vesuvianite, wollastonite

Organic sources:
amber, coral, jet, pearls

Processing

Ideal because of their hardness, some gemstones were used to make tools in prehistoric times. Others, prized for their extraordinary beauty, were used as decorations. Since the supply of good–quality stones could not meet the constantly growing demand, poorer–quality stones began to be used as well. As gemstones were cleaved, engraved, drilled, cut, and carved, the history of gemstone processing began. The method of processing was determined by the properties and quality of a particular stone and by the stone cutter's equipment. The goal was always the same – to create a beautiful stone, one whose color, shape, and optical properties would attract attention. The basic techniques of processing gemstones are cleaving (splitting), then engraving, drilling, cutting, and carving. Nowadays, combinations of these methods are used. Increased knowledge of gemstones and their properties as well as progress in technology have enabled gemstones to be processed into more and more shapes (from decorative engravings to irregular and regular cabochons). The ideal way to process a gemstone is to cut it into specific kinds of facets that take best advantage of the stone's optical properties. Each type of processed shape – cabochon, faceted cut, tumbled stone – requires a different kind of gem rough. While cabochons may contain some cracks, provided the color is neither too light nor too dark, only raw material of the highest quality should be used for faceting (intense color, with no inclusions, cracks, or impurities).

Basic shapes of gemstone cuts

Angular		Oval	Transitional
square	lozenge	oval	oblong
baguette	hexagon	round	marquise (navette)
baton	trapeze	emerald	briolette
regular octagon	keystone	emerald	horseshoe
octagon	pendeloque	cut-cornered lozenge	shield
pentagon	kite	heart	seminavette
triangle	cut-cornered triangle	briolette	keystone

Examples of round gemstone cuts

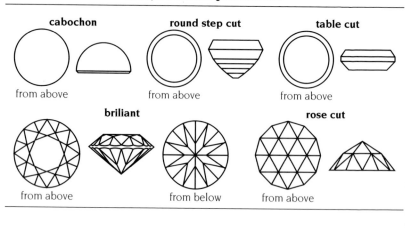

cabochon
from above

round step cut
from above

table cut
from above

briliant
from above   from below

rose cut
from above

Identification

Most gemstones have already been cut by the time they need to be identified. They are also often set in jewelry, so that some of the classic identification methods cannot be used without damaging them. During identification, you should proceed from visual to simple laboratory methods. Various commercially available testers can be also used. When you cannot identify a stone with simple techniques, you should consult an expert gemologist.

Imitations

High prices, inaccessibility, and the lack of high-quality gemstones in particular gradually led to the use of imitation gemstones. Originally, the more available natural stones (or their combinations – doublets, triplets) were used. Later, glass, glazing, artificial materials, and synthetic stones were introduced. Synthetic stones can be divided by chemical composition into two groups: those equivalent to natural gemstones (synthetic diamonds, spinels, corundums, emeralds, zircons, quartzes) and those having no natural counterparts (fianite, YAG, fabulite).

Care of gemstones

Basic rules for taking care of gemstones are given under the heading "Care" for each gemstone. Breaking those rules can change the appearance or quality of a gemstone, and, in extreme cases, can damage or destroy it. Each gemstone should be handled, processed, transported, set, and worn in specific ways, depending on its chemical and physical properties. Proper care of a stone guarantees its stability and durability. The principal dangers for gemstones are sudden shocks, abrasion, and extreme conditions (heat, cold, direct sunlight, harsh chemicals). In order to maintain the impressive look of a gemstone, it should be cleaned properly. Depending on the particular stone, this may be done with ultrasonic or steam cleaning; for more sensitive gemstones, only soap and water should be used.

Gemstones
illustrated

Explanation of symbols:

The following information is presented in the boxes below the heading for each gemstone (left to right):

Preferred ways of processing:

 – faceted cutting

 – cabochon cutting

 – plane cutting and mosaics

 – plastic cutting and glyptics

Optical effects:

 – asterism

 – chatoyancy

Chakra:

See figure on page 17

Sign of zodiac:

See table on page 16

The tab colors around page numbers correspond to those of gemstone divisions shown in the table on page 12; the tab colors around hardness numbers correspond to those of Mohs scale values shown in the same table.

Gemstones illustrated without size or weight are life–size.

Diamond

C

From Greek *adamas* –
"hardest iron or steel, diamond"

Color: colorless, gray, bluish, pinkish, greenish, yellow, orange, lilac, brown to black; very rarely red • **Diaphaneity:** transparent to opaque • **Luster:** adamantine • **Fracture:** conchoidal • **Cleavage:** perfect • **Hardness:** 10, brittle • **Streak:** white • **Specific gravity:** 3.47–3.56 • **Refractive index:** N–2.417 • **Birefringence:** none • **Dispersion:** 0.044 (some data up to 0.0627) • **Pleochroism:** none • **Luminescence:** blue, greenish, yellow • **Chemistry:** color caused by trace amounts of N (yellow), Mn (pink), B (blue); sometimes also Si, Al, Mg, Fe • **Treatment:** irradiation, often combined with temperature changes, diffusion surface treatment

History: The first diamonds came to Europe in the 6th and 5th century B.C. The Natural History Museum in London has a bronze Greek sculpture with rough diamonds dating back to that era. Diamond was later mentioned by Pliny the Elder (23–79 A.D.). Until the 18th century, most diamonds, including most of the famous historical diamonds, came from India.

Diamond crystal, 8 mm, Mir pipe, Mironovo, Yakutia.

Single diamond crystals from different localities; largest, 11 mm.

Then, in 1714, diamonds were discovered in Brazil, and later in South Africa.

Diamonds are connected with many legends, and magical powers were attributed to them. They have always been a symbol of wealth and are found in most crown jewels, important treasuries, and museum collections.

Astrology: birthstone for Leo, Libra (Babylonians), Cancer (Greeks), Aries (Byzantines)

Chakra: base

Healing effects: strengthens entire urinary system; used (often with other gemstones) to treat ailments of stomach, intestines, also epilepsy, Méničre's disease; discharge stone in cold water, then recharge briefly in sunlight

Host rocks: kimberlites, lamproites, placer deposits

Occurrences: Many famous diamonds have come from India, where diamonds have been mined for centuries, especially near Hyderabad, between the Pennar and Sonaken Rivers, where diamonds occur in sandstones, conglomerates, and placer deposits. This region, called Golconda, was already known to Pliny. Recently, diamonds have been mined in Kollur–Ellur (Hyderabad) and near Panna (Madhya Pradesh). Famous stones found in India include the Big Mogul (787.25 ct., found in 1650), the Orloff (189.62 ct., found in 1680), the Nizam (440 ct., found in 1847), the blue Hope (44.52 ct.), Koh–i–Noor (105.60 ct.), and the yellow Florentine (137.27 ct.). Historically important deposits were found in Indonesia (Borneo). In 1714, diamonds were discovered in Brazilian river sediments, together with gold and quartz, near Diamantina in Minas Gerais and later also in Bahía.

Brazil has recently become an important producer of technical–grade diamonds (***carbonados***), the largest of which weighed 3,148 ct., and has produced many large gem–quality diamonds, such as the President Vargas (726.6 ct., cut into 29 separate stones), the Goiás (600 ct., of which only a 8 ct. fragment remains), and the Darcy Vargas (460 ct.). Colored diamonds, such as the lilac Tiros (12.25 ct.), the pink Abaeté (238 ct.), the yellow–green Maximilian (50 ct.), and the light blue Brasilia (176.2 ct.), have also been found here. One of the most important diamond producers is South Africa. The world's largest and most beautiful diamonds have come from the basins of the Orange and Vaal Rivers. South African occurrences are not limited to placers. Primary deposits in kimberlite pipes are also mined, the most famous being Premier Mine, whose cross–sectional dimensions are 924 x 462 meters (3,030 x 1,515 feet). The world's largest diamond, the Cullinan (3,106 ct.), was found there. Many South African diamonds are in crown jewels or museum

Diamond octahedron in kimberlite, 10 mm, South Africa.

collections. Important stones (weights are of rough pieces before cutting) are the Excelsior (995.2 ct., found in 1893), the pink Jubilee (650.8 ct., found in 1895, and recently called the Reitz diamond), the Jonker (726 ct., found in 1934), and the Dutoispan (616 ct., found in 1974). Diamonds were later found in Lesotho and Botswana. Significant recent diamond production comes from the western offshore zone in southern Africa (South Africa, Namibia, Angola). These diamonds are of high quality and weigh up to 70 ct. Large placer deposits (approx. 390,000 km^2 or 150,600 mi^2) have been found in the sediments of the Kasai and Chicapa Rivers in the Democratic Republic of the Congo (Zaire) and Angola. Alluvial deposits are also known in the Central African Republic, the Republic of the Congo, and Gabon. Smaller deposits are located in Ghana,

Sierra Leone (Star of Sierra Leone, 968.90 ct.), Ivory Coast, Liberia, Mali, Guinea, Senegal, Tanzania, and Zimbabwe.

At present, China and Russia are very important diamond producers. Diamonds are mined in Shandong and Yunnan provinces and on Hainan Island. In Russia, where there are more that 120 known kimberlite pipes, diamonds were discovered in the Vilui River basin in 1949, and later in other locations. Many Russian diamonds weigh over 200 ct., such as the Star of Yakutia (232 ct.). Colored diamonds are also known from Russia, such as the green Miner (44.62 ct.) or the light yellow octahedron Marie (106 ct.). Less important occurrences are located in Venezuela, Surinam, French Guiana, the United States, and Australia.

Processing: faceted cuts; approximately 20% of diamond production is of gem quality

Similar minerals: none

Imitations: synthetic diamond, rock crystal, goshenite, cassiterite, cerussite, sapphire, scheelite, topaz, zircon, synthetic cubic zirconia, YAG, GGG, rutile, lead glass

Identification: hardness, refractive index, luster, thermal conductivity

Care: Buy faceted stones only with a certificate (some diamonds have their ID number engraved by laser on the girdle). Because they are brittle, it is important to protect diamonds from sudden shocks and sudden temperature changes. There are no cleaning problems unless stone contains inclusions.

Colored brilliant cut diamonds; largest, 1.35 ct.

Ruby

(corundum variety)

Al_2O_3

From Latin
rubeus – "reddish"

History: This intensely red stone has been highly prized since ancient times. The oldest written records report a ruby mine in Burma. Through the trade routes, rubies reached the royal courts and temples of ancient Egypt and Greece. A favorite stone of the Romans, it was originally cut into an oval shape, and especially large and fine rubies had their own names. Ruby was considered a stone of life, which strengthened the heart and restored vitality. Magi-

Color: red with modifying secondary hues • **Diaphaneity:** transparent to translucent, opaque • **Luster:** glassy, adamantine • **Fracture:** conchoidal, uneven • **Cleavage:** none • **Hardness:** 9, brittle • **Streak:** white • **Specific gravity:** 3.97–4.05 • **Refractive index:** N_e–1.760–1.768, N_o–1.768–1.778 • **Birefringence:** –0.008 • **Dispersion:** 0.018 • **Pleochroism:** strong – orange to crimson red – dichroic • **Chemistry:** color caused by trace amounts of Cr, Fe • **Special features:** asterism, rare chatoyancy, trillings (*Trapiche ruby*) • **Treatment:** heating, irradiation, diffusion coloring

Star ruby, 1.20 ct.

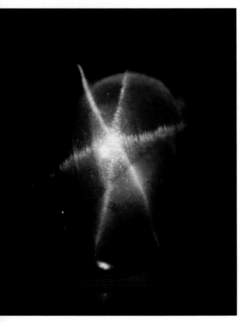

cal powers were attributed to it especially in ancient times and the Middle Ages. Ruby was said to protect believers from the devil and the plague.

Astrology: birthstone for Scorpio, Leo (Babylonians), Cancer (Byzantines)

Chakra: base

Healing effects: strengthens heart, circulation; used to treat mental lethargy, also eye problems; discharge stone in cold water, then recharge briefly in sunlight

Host rocks: metamorphic rocks, pegmatites, placer deposits

Occurrences: Most of the large and fine rubies in the past (especially between 1899 and 1928) came from the metamorphic rocks and skarns of Mogok region in Burma, an area about 400 km^2 (155 mi^2). Rubies from these parent rocks were transported to placers. Reportedly, mining activity here dates back to the Bronze Age, with the largest rubies weighing up to 40 ct. and with many becoming crown jewels. Rubies are also mined in Thailand, near Chanthaburi and Battambang, but they have a slight brownish tint. Another locality is in Cambodia. Sri Lanka's gem–bearing gravels, a territory greater than 2,000 km^2 (770 mi^2), are a historically important mining area for rubies, where stones with asterism or a cat's–eye effect have been found. Smaller occurrences are known

Ruby crystals on matrix, 42 mm high, Mysore, India.

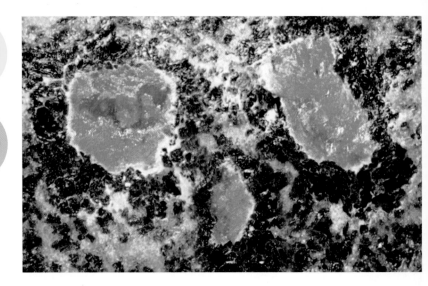

Ruby crystals embedded in zoisitic matrix, 100 mm wide, Tanzania.

from Jagdalek, Afghanistan, in the Hunza River valley, Pakistan, from the corundum–bearing veins of Tamil Nadu and Mysore, India, and from the gold–bearing sediments of Cowee Creek, North Carolina. Marbles in Harts Ridge in North Territory, Australia, have also produced some rubies. Rubies are commonly found in Madagascar near Ankaratra and Vontivotonye, both from primary deposits and from placers. Tanzanian localities include

Ruby embedded in matrix, Kola Peninsula, Russia.

Motombo, Kwakonje, Mahenge, Gairo, the Umba River basin, where corundum crystals of different colors reach 4 cm in size, and the Olgira and Lossonogoi Hills, where large red ruby crystals are found embedded in a green zoisitic rock used as a decorative stone. Gem–quality rubies come also from the Sombule gravels of Zambia and from the Chimwadzulu Mts. of Malawi. Additional African localities are in the Democratic Republic of the Congo (Zaire), Angola, and the Republic of the Congo. Russia has produced some ruby crystals from the Polar Urals. Other European ruby occurrences are in Norway and Finland. Big, light red to pink ruby crystals (up to 15 cm) were found near Prilep, Macedonia. Large, unique, gem–quality crystals and cut stones often have their own names and serve as the premier stones of crown jewels and museum collections. One of the most important rubies is the North Star, a purple–red star ruby (166 ct.) from the collection of the American Museum of Natural History in

New York. Another, the Edith Hagen de Long (100 ct.), comes from the same collection. The Rosser Reeves star ruby (139 ct.) from Sri Lanka is at the Smithsonian Institution in Washington, D.C., while the semitransparent Edward ruby (167 ct.) is at the Natural History Museum in London. One of the largest known cut rubies – an irregular cut measuring 39.5 x 36.5 x 14 mm and weighing 250 ct. – can be found in the St. Wenceslas crown in Prague. Many unique rubies are in the treasuries of Indian rajas and of the former Shah of Iran. Large ruby crystals weighing over 500 ct. before cutting are exceedingly rare. One is at the Natural History Museum in London, a ruby Buddha sculpture from Burma weighing 690 g. In 1934, a star ruby weighing 593.4 g was found in Sri Lanka.

Processing: faceted cuts, cabochons, carvings

Similar minerals: spinel, pink tourmaline (rubellite), pyrope

Imitations: synthetic corundum, spinel, glass, garnet, tourmaline

Care: Protect ruby from high temperatures, which can cause stones to change color. There are no cleaning problems unless stone contains inclusions.

Faceted ruby, Thailand, 3.37 ct.

Sapphire

(corundum variety)

Al_2O_3

From Greek *sappheiros*
– "lapis lazuli, sapphire"

Color: different hues of blue, purple, blue–purple, green, yellow, colorless (*leucosapphire*), orange, pink–orange (*padparadscha*) • **Diaphaneity:** transparent to translucent, opaque • **Luster:** glassy, dull • **Fracture:** conchoidal, uneven • **Cleavage:** none • **Hardness:** 9, brittle • **Streak:** white • **Specific gravity:** 3.99–4.10 • **Refractive index:** N_e–1.760–1.770, N_o–1.768–1.779 • **Birefringence:** 0.008–0.009 • **Pleochroism:** distinct – different hues depending on color of stone • **Luminescence:** sometimes purple or orange • **Chemistry:** color caused by trace amounts of Fe, Ti, Cr, Mn, V, U • **Special features:** asterism, rare chatoyancy • **Treatment:** heating, irradiation, diffusion coloring

History: Sapphire's beauty and exceptional properties have fascinated man since early historical times. In the past, most of the blue gemstones were called sapphires. Only since the 19th century have sapphire and ruby been recognized as varieties of corundum. A symbol of wealth and believed to relieve pain and prevent disputes, sapphire was thought to bring power, honor, and immortality to its owner. In the Middle Ages, as the "bishop's stone," sapphire represented heaven and the highest spiritual values.

Astrology: birthstone for Capricorn, Sagittarius (Greeks), Aquarius (Byzantines)
Chakra: throat

Healing effects: lowers blood pressure; used to treat insomnia, sometimes can-

Rough sapphires; largest piece, 5 mm, Gem Mountain, Montana.

cer; discharge stone in cold water, then recharge briefly in sunlight

Host rocks: metamorphic rocks, pegmatites, alkaline basalts, placers

Occurrences: The gem–bearing gravels of Sri Lanka, over an area of about 2,000 km² (770 mi²), have long been mined for sapphires and leucosapphires. Large, although not always gemmy sapphires have been found there from time to time, the largest reportedly weighing about 20 kg. Gemmy sapphires weighing 144 and 300 ct., respectively, were found in 1974.

Another very important area for sapphire production is the Mogok region of northern Burma, where sapphires have long been mined from marbles and skarns over an area of about 400 km² (155 mi²), although sapphires were always rarer than rubies. A star sapphire weighing 12.6 kg was found there in 1966. Primary and placer deposits of sapphires, limited to Tertiary basalt lava flows, are located in Thailand, Laos, Vietnam, and Cambodia. The Pailin deposit in Cambodia has been important since 1874. Thai sapphires

9

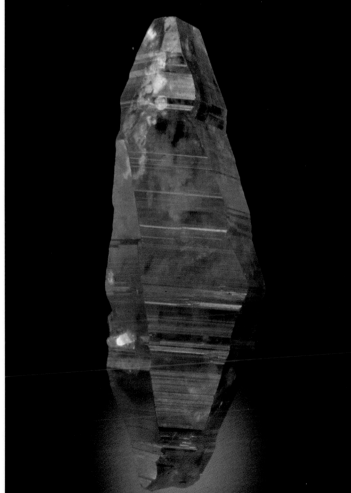

Typical sapphire crystal, 40 mm long, Glubkka, Val i vaya, Uva province, Sri Lanka.

come from the Chanthaburi and Battambang regions, the largest stone weighing 150 ct.

Northern India (Kashmir and Jammu) is also a productive area. Lower–quality sapphires have been produced in southern China. Some sapphire finds are known from Renfrew, Ontario, Canada. Deep blue sapphires were found in Matto Grosso, Brazil. Recently, important sapphire production has come from Queensland and New South Wales, Australia, where deposits in alkaline basalts of light blue to greenish, often zonal sapphires weather out to placers. African sapphire deposits are located in Mozambique, Rwanda, Cameroon, South Africa, and Namibia, as well as Tanzania's Umba River basin. Zimbabwe has produced sapphire crystals up to 7 cm long, the largest one weighing

Gold ring with baroque pearls and black sapphire (Thailand), by Karel Valter, Geneva, Switzerland.

Star sapphire, 2.20 ct.

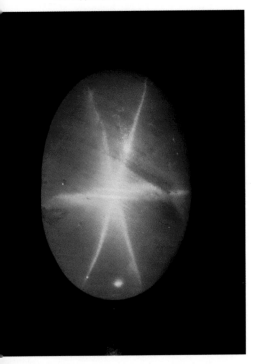

3,100 ct. Smaller localities are known from Malawi, Zambia, the Republic of the Congo, and Madagascar (rare crystals over 10 cm long). Large sapphire concentrations have been found in Russia, especially in pegmatites of the Ural Mts., and in the alkaline pegmatites of the Kola Peninsula, where crystals up to 5 kg were found, although not of gem quality. Historical finds of nice sapphires are reported from the Jizera river sediments in the Czech Republic (locality Jizerská louka). Many unique stones have their own names and were used in crown jewels. Dating back to 1042, the deep blue sapphire of St. Edward (167 ct.) in the center of the cross on the British imperial crown is one of the most remarkable, as is the Steward sapphire (104 ct.) set in the same crown. Two large sapphires (258 and 200 ct.) are in the Russian imperial crown, held in the Diamond Fund in Moscow. The St. Wenceslas crown in Prague also has two large sapphires (330 and 280 ct.), from Sri Lanka. Unique star sapphires, the Star of India (536 ct.) and the Midnight Star (116 ct.), can be found at the American Museum of Natural History in New York, while the deep blue Star of Asia (330 ct.) is located at the Smithsonian Institution in Washington, D.C. Famous sapphires have also come from the United States

(Rock Creek and Yogo Gulch, Montana; North Carolina), where three large sapphires were carved into the heads of the three presidents – Washington (1,997 ct.), Lincoln (2,302 ct.), and Eisenhower (2,097 ct.). Many large and unique stones are in private collections in Iran, India, and Turkey.

Processing: faceted cuts, cabochons, engravings

Similar minerals: spinel, cordierite, zoisite, tourmaline (indicolite), benitoite, topaz, kyanite, zircon, tanzanite

Imitations: synthetic corundum, doublets, glass

Identification: hardness, specific gravity, optical properties (absorption spectrum)

Care: Protect sapphire from excessive heat, which can cause stones to lose color. There are no cleaning problems unless stone contains inclusions.

Various colors of sapphires; largest, 8.85 ct., Montana.

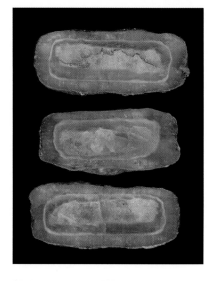

"Watermelon sapphire," 20 mm wide, India.

Chrysoberyl

$BeAl_2O_4$

From Greek *chrysos*
– "gold, yellow" + "beryl"

History: In the past, chrysoberyl was considered beryl and set as such in jewelry. The cymophane variety was especially prized.

Astrology: birthstone for Gemini

Chakras: heart, navel (yellow varieties)

Healing effects: strong suppressant effects; yellow varieties used to treat stomach spasms; discharge stone in lukewarm water, then recharge briefly in sunlight

Host rocks: pegmatites, metamorphic rocks, placers

Occurrences: Chrysoberyl and cymophane have long been found in the gem–bearing gravels near Ratnapura, Sri Lanka. Cymophane has occurred also in southern India near Trivandruma. Colorless chrysoberyls are known from the Mogok region of Burma and from China, and have been

Color: colorless, yellow, golden yellow, green, brown • **Diaphaneity:** transparent, translucent • **Luster:** glassy • **Fracture:** conchoidal • **Cleavage:** good to poor • **Hardness:** 8.5, brittle • **Streak:** white • **Specific gravity:** 3.68–3.80 • **Refractive index:** N_p–1.746, N_m–1.748, N_g–1.756 • **Birefringence:** 0.008–0.012 • **Dispersion:** 0.015 • **Pleochroism:** distinct • **Luminescence:** yellow–green • **Chemistry:** color caused by Cr, Fe^{3+} • **Special features:** chatoyancy (**cymophane** or cat's–eye variety), rare asterism • **Treatment:** not known

discovered in the gem–bearing gravels of Zimbabwe (Somabule), South Africa, and Madagascar. Yellow chrysoberyls come from the pegmatites and placers in Minas Gerais, Brazil. A crystal 6.4 cm in diameter

Chrysoberyl sixling, together with a cut stone (10.77 ct.), Itaguacu, Espírito Santo, Minas Gerais, Brazil.

Chrysoberyl cut, 11.5 ct.

was found in Itaguacu in Espírito Santo. Some localities are reported from the United States (Connecticut, Maine, New York, and Colorado). Yellow–green chrysoberyls occur in the Anakia region of Australia. Chrysoberyl has been described from Maršíkov, Moravia, Czech Republic, but it is not of gem quality. Some chrysoberyls have been found in Japan and the Democratic Republic of the Congo (Zaire), as well. Unique chrysoberyls are highly valued. The Hope chrysoberyl (45 ct.) from the collection of the Natural History Museum in London is one of the best known. A faceted yellow–green stone from Sri Lanka (29.4 ct.) is in the same collection, while a very fine yellow–green cut chrysoberyl weighing 74.4 ct. is at the American Museum of Natural History in New York. Cut stones weighing 171.5 ct. (Maharani) and 58.2 ct., both chatoyant, as well as yellow–green (114.3 ct.) and green (120.5 ct.) faceted stones from Sri Lanka, are at the Smithsonian Institution in Washington, D.C. Sri Lanka also produced cat's–eye chrysoberyls weighing 475 and 313.2 ct., the latter in the British imperial treasury. Reportedly, the world's largest faceted stone weighs 245 ct. and also comes from Sri Lanka. A chrysoberyl weighing 8 kg was found in Brazil in 1828.
Processing: faceted cuts, cabochons

Similar minerals: andalusite, scapolite, grossular
Imitations: synthetic corundum
Identification: hardness, specific gravity, optical methods
Care: There are no cleaning problems unless stone contains inclusions.

Chrysoberyl cat's–eye – cymophane.

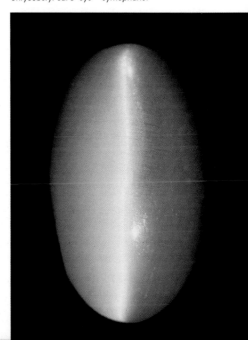

Alexandrite

(chrysoberyl variety)

$BeAl_2O_4$

After Czar
Alexander II

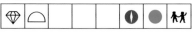

History: Discovered in the Ural Mts. in 1834, alexandrite is the most valuable variety of chrysoberyl. According to legend, it was an emerald by day and a purple amethyst by night. This effect was later named the "alexandrite effect." The stone was believed to symbolize life and its metamophoses.

Astrology: birthstone for Gemini

Chakra: heart

Healing effects: regulates blood formation; cleanses, strengthens veins, arteries; discharge stone in lukewarm water, then recharge briefly in sunlight

Host rocks: metamorphic rocks, pegmatites, placers

Occurrences: The most important, and for many years the world's only known, alexandrite deposit is located in the Tokovaya River basin in the Ural Mts., Russia (Malyshevo). One of the best–preserved specimens is a matrix alexandrite called Kochubei, measuring 25 x 15 cm and weighing 5.38 kg, with crystals up to 6 x 3 cm, in Moscow's Fersman Mineralogical Museum. Malyshevo alexandrites occur in mica

Color: deep green to emerald green (daylight), purple–red to purple (artificial light) • **Diaphaneity:** transparent, translucent • **Luster:** glassy • **Fracture:** conchoidal • **Cleavage:** good to poor • **Hardness:** 8.5, brittle • **Streak:** white • **Specific gravity:** 3.71 • **Refractive index:** N_p–1.746, N_m–1.748, N_g–1.755 • **Birefringence:** 0.008–0.010 • **Dispersion:** 0.015 • **Pleochroism:** very strong – emerald green (daylight), orange to purple–red (artificial light) – dichroic • **Luminescence:** weak red, mostly none • **Chemistry:** color caused by Cr, Fe^{3+}; heat–sensitive • **Special features:** alexandrite effect, rare chatoyancy • **Treatment:** not known

schists together with emerald and phenakite. Chatoyant alexandrites are very rare. Good rough material was later found in the placers of Minas Gerais, Bahía, Brazil, and in the Latpandura region of Sri Lanka. Alexandrite was found together with cymophane in the Tsarasatro and Ambatosoratra regions of Madagascar, and together with emeralds in the gem–bearing Somabule gravels of Zimbabwe. Some occurrences are known from India and South Africa, as well. Recently, gemmy alexandrites were found near Manyara Lake in Tanzania. Rare alexandrites come from Tasmania. Cut alexan-

Faceted alexandrites in artificial light, Tokovaya River, Ural Mts., Russia.

Same cut stones in daylight.

drites from Sri Lanka can be found at the Natural History Museum in London (43 and 27.5 ct.) and the Smithsonian Institution in Washington, D.C. (65.7 ct.).

Processing: faceted cuts, cabochons
Similar minerals: andalusite, garnet with alexandrite effect
Imitations: synthetic ruby, doublets, synthetic alexandrite, natural and synthetic corundum, spinel with alexandrite effect
Identification: hardness, specific gravity, optical methods
Care: Alexandrite may lose color during heating. There are no cleaning problems unless stone contains inclusions.

Typical alexandrite sixling, 50 mm wide, Tokovaya River, Ural Mts., Russia.

Druse of alexandrite crystals on matrix, 75 mm wide, Tokovaya River, Ural Mts., Russia.

Spinel

$MgAl_2O_4$

From Latin *spinella*, dim.
of *spina* – "thorn" for crystal shape

History: All red gemstones were originally called *carbunculi*, including spinel, which received its name only much later. Always popular, and present in many pieces of old jewelry, spinel was mistaken for ruby, most notably in the British crown jewels.

Chakra: base

Healing effects: promotes circulation; used to treat anemia, also mental depression; discharge stone for extended time in running water, then recharge briefly in sunlight

Host rocks: contact metamorphic rocks, placers

Occurrences: The most important spinel finds, some chatoyant and very similar to rubies in color, have come from the gem–bearing gravels of Burma and Sri Lanka. Gem–quality spinels also occur in

Color: colorless, yellow, green, blue, red, purple, pink; also brown and black (*ceylonite* or *pleonaste*) • **Diaphaneity:** transparent to translucent, opaque • **Luster:** glassy • **Fracture:** conchoidal • **Cleavage:** none • **Hardness:** 8, brittle • **Streak:** white • **Specific gravity:** 3.58–4.06 • **Refractive index:** N–1.710–1.735 • **Birefringence:** none • **Dispersion:** 0.020 • **Pleochroism:** none • **Luminescence:** sometimes yellow–green, red, orange, mostly none • **Chemistry:** color caused by trace amounts of Fe^{3+} and Cu (green), Fe^{2+} (blue), Fe^{2+} and Cr (red) • **Special features:** asterism, occasional chatoyancy • **Treatment:** sometimes heating

Thailand (near Bo Ploi), Cambodia, and Laos. African spinels have been found mainly in Madagascar and Kenya (Ngorigaishi). An ancient locality exists in Afghanistan. Gemmy spinels occur in many localities in Minas Gerais and Bahía, Brazil. The United States has produced some

Typical intergrowth of spinel crystals, 7 mm, Mogok, Burma.

spinels from different localities in California, Montana, New York (crystals up to 14 kg from Amity), New Jersey, Virginia, and North Carolina. Canadian spinels in crystals up to 5 cm were found in marbles at Glancoe in the Northwest Territories. Spinel is also reported from Greenland and from Russia (Aldan). The pink cut stones from Tajikistan (Pamir Mts.) are world-famous, although they rarely reach 100 ct. A spinel weighing 5.1 kg was re-

ported from Russia in 1986. Fairly rare spinels are known from Norway (crystals up to 3 cm from Akeru), the Czech Republic (historical finds with sapphires from Jizerská louka), Finland, Italy, and Germany. Indian and Australian localities are of lesser importance. Many spinels became important parts of crown jewels. The deep red spinel (398.7 ct.) of the czar's crown in the Diamond Fund in Moscow is probably the most famous. Two large spinels are in the British imperial crown. The Black Prince "ruby" weighs approximately 170 ct., and the Timur "ruby" about 361 ct. Large spinels are also set in the St. Wenceslas crown in Prague (45 in all), and the Natural History Museum in London has two large stones (355 and 520 ct.) in its collection.

Processing: faceted cuts, cabochons
Similar minerals: ruby, sapphire, zircon, amethyst, garnet
Imitations: garnets, synthetic spinel
Identification: hardness, specific gravity, optical methods
Care: Spinel may lose color when heated. There are no cleaning problems unless stone contains inclusions.

Single spinel crystal, 33 mm high.

Cut spinel, 3.94 ct.

Topaz

$Al_2SiO_4(F,OH)_2$

After Topazos Island
in Red Sea

History: Currently a very popular gemstone, and called by many different local names depending on its source, topaz has lent its name to other yellow and green stones in times past. Said to calm stormy seas, topaz was believed to endow men with wisdom, generosity, and intellect – and women with beauty and fertility.

Astrology: birthstone for Libra, Scorpio (Babylonians)

Chakras: navel (yellow varieties), throat (blue varieties)

Color: colorless, yellow, golden yellow, pink, bluish, red–orange, purple, greenish, brown; also multicolored • **Diaphaneity:** transparent, translucent • **Luster:** glassy • **Fracture:** conchoidal • **Cleavage:** perfect • **Hardness:** 8 • **Streak:** white • **Specific gravity:** 3.5–3.6 • **Refractive index:** N_p–1.606–1.629, N_m–1.609–1.631, N_g–1.616–1.638 • **Birefringence:** 0.009–0.011 • **Dispersion:** 0.014 • **Pleochroism:** distinct – different hues depending on color of stone • **Luminescence:** golden yellow, creamy, green • **Chemistry:** color caused by trace amounts of Fe, Cr, Ti, V • **Special features:** rare chatoyancy • **Treatment:** irradiation, heating

Topaz with smoky quartz, 50 mm long, Tonoka, Myama, Japan.

Topaz crystal on smoky quartz, 70 mm long, Murzinka, Ural Mts., Russia.

Healing effects: lowers blood pressure; used to treat insomnia, also lack of appetite, gout, liver diseases; discharge stone in running water, then briefly recharge in sunlight

Host rocks: pegmatites, placers, igneous rocks, greisens, metamorphic rocks

Occurrences: The most important topaz producer is Brazil. Colorless, yellow, brownish, and red varieties (**Brazilian rubies**) are known from Mina Saramenha, Don Bosco, Virgem da Lapa, and other localities in Minas Gerais. The Marambaya region has produced blue and colorless topazes, while golden topazes are known from Teófilo

Otoni. Arassuai River sediments are also a source for topaz. Many unique, historically famous topazes come from Brazil, such as the colorless Braganza topaz (1,680 ct., found in 1740), set in the Portuguese crown and originally thought to be a diamond. Large topaz crystals and cut stones are the highlights of many museum collections. The Field Natural History Museum in Chicago has a topaz weighing 5,890 ct. The Natural History Museum in London has two cut topazes weighing 614 and 1,300 ct., as well as a light blue topaz crystal from Marambaya that measures 18 x 13 x 5 cm and weighs 3.6 kg, and another weighing 13 kg. The unique yellow Santa Rosa topaz, measuring 43 x 41 x 40 cm and weighing

117 kg, a crystal measuring 80 x 60 x 60 cm and weighing 300 kg, and a colorless cut topaz called the Princess of Brazil, weighing 22,000 ct., are all housed at the American Museum of Natural History in New York. The largest known cut topaz, called the Champagne Topaz, weighs 36,853 ct. and comes from Brazil, as does a huge crystal measuring 2 x 1.8 m and weighing 5 t (5.5 short tons), found in 1986. Many localities in the United States have produced fine topazes, such as Pikes Peak, Colorado; San Diego Co., California (Little Three Mine); Streeter, Texas; and Stoneham, Maine. Wine yellow and brown topazes are known from the Thomas Range, Utah (crystals up to 5 cm). Blue topazes come from New Hampshire and Virginia (Herbb, with crystals up to 28 cm). Light red topazes are found in Mexico (San Luis Potosí, Durango). Russia

Topaz with albite and muscovite, 45 mm long, Shengus, Pakistan.

Rare pink topaz, 26 mm long, Sanarka River basin, Ural Mts., Russia.

is another important topaz producer, with most localities in the Ural Mts. and Transbaikalia. The Sanarka River sediments are famous for pink topaz, while some topaz crystals from Murzinka, Alabashka, and Yushkovaya – all four localities in the Ural Mts. – have reached 100 kg. Sherlovaya Gora in Transbaikalia has produced some bluish topazes. Colorless, blue, pinkish, brownish, or bicolored topazes from the pegmatites near Volodarsk Volynskii in the Zhitomir region of Ukraine have sometimes exceeded 100 kg. Many large crystals and cut stones of Russian and Ukrainian topaz are in Moscow's Fersman Mineralogical Museum, such as the topaz Golden Forest (5.38 kg), the Fairy Tale (2.81 kg), the light blue Fersman topaz (2.11 kg), a wine yellow topaz weighing 13.1 kg, found in 1840, a green–blue topaz weighing 32 kg, found in 1911, and a light blue topaz from Volodarsk Volynskii weighing 117 kg and measuring 82 x 37 x 35 cm, found in 1964. Historically, Sri Lanka has produced the most famous gemmy topazes, with colorless, golden yellow, and light green stones coming from the gem–bearing gravels near Ratnapura and Balangoda. Other Asian occurrences are in India (Orissa) and Burma (Mogok region). Rare pink–red topazes from Mardan, Pakistan, have reached over 4 cm in size, pink topazes are also known from China. Light blue crystals were found in Mongolia. Japan has also produced yellow, brown, and green topazes near Takayama, Ishigura, and Naegi. The best African topazes occur in Madagascar, where large crystals are known from Mahabe, Scarane, Ikopa, Belamo. Topazes are also known from Kenya (Embu region) and Namibia (Spitzkopje), with nice blue stones coming from Nigeria and Zimbabwe (Scambula region). The best–known Australian localites are in Tasmania, New South Wales (Tinga region), and Western

Australia. The classic European locality is Schneckenstein in Saxony, Germany, where topaz has been mined since the 18th century. The crystals are wine yellow, reaching several centimeters in length. Other European occurrences are in Norway (Iveland region, with crystals up to 80 kg), Northern Ireland, Scotland, England, and the Czech Republic.

Processing: faceted cuts, cabochons, engravings

Similar minerals: sapphire, goshenite, aquamarine, phenakite, rock crystal, citrine

Imitations: synthetic corundum, glass, quartz

Identification: hardness, specific gravity, cleavage, optical methods

Care: Protect topaz's perfect cleavage from sudden shocks and sudden temperature changes. Color may fade in sunlight. Treated stones may also fade in time, and some may be slightly radioactive. There are no cleaning problems unless stone contains inclusions.

Cut topazes of different colors; largest, 132 ct., Volodarsk Volynskii, Ukraine.

Emerald
(beryl variety)

$Be_3Al_2Si_6O_{18}$

From Greek *smaragdos* – "emerald"

History: Queen of the gemstones, emerald has been known, mined, and used for jewelry, amulets, and religious objects since earliest history, and unique emeralds are preserved in many treasuries and mu-

Color: emerald green • **Diaphaneity:** transparent to translucent, opaque • **Luster:** glassy • **Fracture:** conchoidal, uneven • **Cleavage:** indistinct • **Hardness:** 7.5–8 (often lower due to inclusions) • **Streak:** white • **Specific gravity:** 2.67–2.90 • **Refractive index:** N_e–1.569–1.585, N_o–1.574–1.592 • **Birefringence:** –0.005–0.009 • **Dispersion:** 0.014 • **Pleochroism:** distinct • **Luminescence:** mostly none, sometimes orange–red • **Chemistry:** color caused by trace amounts of Cr, V • **Special features:** chatoyancy, trillings (***Trapiche emerald***), rare asterism • **Treatment:** oiling, fracture filling with resins or epoxy, sometimes dyeing

Emerald crystal, 30 mm long, Habachtal, Austria.

seum collections around the world. Found in the Egyptian pharaohs' graves and excavated from Pompeii and Herculaneum, emerald is mentioned in the Bible and belongs to the apostolic stones (St. Thomas). Large numbers of rough emeralds have been discovered on the sea bottom between America and Europe. The stone's unmistakable color is widely recognized as a distinct hue of green (emerald green).

Astrology: birthstone for Leo, Cancer (Babylonians)

Chakra: heart

Healing effects: strengthens memory; sharpens mental acuity; relieves flatulence, heartburn, also insomnia; used to treat gastric ulcers, ailments of gallbladder, liver, heart, eyes; discharge stone in running water, then recharge briefly in sunlight

Host rocks: metamorphic biotite schists, marbles, hydrothermal veins, pegmatites

Occurrences: The oldest known, and for a long time the only, emerald mines are located in Jebel Zabarah and Jebel Sikat in Upper Egypt. The "Cleopatra" mines were first worked by the ancient Egyptians, then by Greeks, Romans, Arabs, and Turks. Forgotten in the Middle Ages, they were rediscovered only in the 19th century. Their

Typical emerald crystal on matrix, 20 mm long, Muzo, Boyacá, Colombia.

most beautiful emeralds are supposedly preserved in the Turkish sultan's treasury in Topkapi Palace in Istambul and in the treasury of the Shah of Iran. The emerald lens that (according to Pliny) Nero used for watching the gladiator games was probably cut from material from this locality, as were engravings of the Roman emperor Hadrian and his wife, Sabina. The world's most important source of emeralds has been Colombia, where they were mined by the Incas even before the Spaniards arrived in 1537. Famous Colombian emerald mines are at Muzo (NW of Bogotá), Chivor, Coscuez, and Peña Blanca. Emerald crystals and cut stones are preserved in the cathedral treasuries of Spain, the treasury of Iran, and many museums. The Emilia (7,025 ct.), the Austrian emerald (2,681 ct.), the carved vase Colombia (1,976 ct.), the Devonshire emerald (crystal weighing 1,384 ct.), and the Patricia (630 ct.) are among the largest. Other important deposits are located in Brazil, at Sohoto, Alagoihas, Carnaíba, Pilao Arcado (Bahía), Pela Ema, Santa Annados Ferros (Minas Gerais), and Santa Terezinha (Goiás), among others. The largest known Brazilian emerald crystal weighs 6,300 ct. The United States has also produced fine emeralds from Hiddenite (North Carolina) and Mt. Mica (Newry, Maine), whose largest stones include Stephenson's emerald (1,438 ct.), the Hiddenite emerald (1,276 ct.), and the Stolen emerald (1,270 ct.). Important European emerald localities are Habachtal in the Austrian Alps, known since Roman times and the Tokovaya River basin, Ural Mts., Russia, where Malyshevo, the deepest emerald mine in the world (350 m or 1,150 ft), has produced such stones as the Kokovina (1,100 ct.) and the Famous Ural (3,362 ct.) Important emerald mining sites in Africa are Micu in Zambia, Novello Cleims, Shikwande, and Mayfiel Fanu in Zimbabwe, Leydsdorpe in South Africa, and other localities in Nigeria, Ghana, Tanzania, and Namibia. Asian occurrences are concentrated in India (Ajmer, Udaipur), Pakistan (Gudjarat – Kilh, Gandar, Tora–Tiga), and Afghanistan (Paudshere). Australia (Broken Hill, Aga–Kau, Emnanvill, Vegesatle

Emerald crystals in mica schist, 60 mm long, Izumrudnye kopi, Ural Mts., Russia.

Trapiche emeralds; largest, 28.02 ct., Peña Blanca, Muzo, Boyacá, Colombia.

Cut emerald, 5.28 ct., Colombia.

Creek, Glen Creek) is now also an important emerald producer.

Processing: High–quality stones are cut into "emerald" cuts; clear transparent stones are also cut into brilliants; lower –quality material is used for tumbled stones – cabochons, balls, and other objects. Emerald is set mainly as a solitary center stone in jewelry, surrounded with diamonds, mounted in gold.

Similar minerals: verdelite, apatite, demantoid, uvarovite, diopside, dioptase, grossular, hiddenite, olivine

Imitations: synthetic emerald (Chatham emerald, Linde emerald, Gilson emerald), green spinel, glass doublets cemented together with colored cement

Identification: optical methods, emerald loupe, Chelsea filter

Care: A very fragile stone, emerald must be protected from sudden shocks, overheating, and pressure. Clean in soap and water only; do not use ultrasonic or steam cleaning. Stable in common acids, it loses color at temperatures over 700 °C. Oiled stones may also fade.

Aquamarine

(beryl variety)

$Be_3Al_2Si_6O_{18}$

From Latin *aqua marina*
— *"seawater," hence "blue–green"*

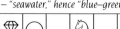

History: One of the most popular gem-stones, aquamarine was especially valued in the Middle Ages. The first lenses for eyeglasses were cut from it around 1300. According to medieval astrologers, aqua-marine had the power to calm the sea, to guarantee friendship and justice, and to banish the troubles of its owners. It was named by Boëtius de Boodt in 1604 and is often found in large crystals having names and history of their own.

Astrology: birthstone for Aquarius, Libra (medieval astrologers)

Chakra: throat

Healing effects: strengthens heart; used to treat ailments of lungs, skin, nerves; dis-charge stone in running water, then re-charge repeatedly in sunlight

Host rocks: pegmatites, placers

Occurrences: World–famous aquamarine

Color: light to deep blue (***maxixe***); also green–blue; color may fade in sunlight • **Diaphaneity:** transparent, translucent • **Luster:** glassy • **Fracture:** conchoidal, uneven • **Cleavage:** indistinct • **Hardness:** 7.5–8 • **Streak:** white • **Specific gravity:** 2.68–2.80 • **Refractive index:** N_e–1.567–1.583, N_o–1.572–1.590 • **Biferingence:** 0.005–0.009 • **Dispersion:** 0.014 • **Pleochroism:** weak to distinct • **Luminescence:** none • **Chemistry:** color caused by Fe^{2+}, Fe^{3+} • **Special features:** occasional chatoyancy • **Treatment:** heating

deposits occur in Brazil, especially in the pegmatites of Minas Gerais, near Teófilo Otoni, Diamantina, Rio Doce, and Sapu-caia. Aquamarine is here associated with morganite, lepidolite, sometimes kunzite (Itambacuri). Other Brazilian localities in-clude Bahía (Veruga, Bomu Jesus da Lapa) and Espírito Santo. Aquamarine–bearing placers have been mined in Rio Pedro and Rio Contas (Bahía) and, since 1909, in the Marambaya River basin, where a crystal weighing 110.5 kg was found.

Cut aquamarine, 59.8 ct., Dassu, Pakistan.

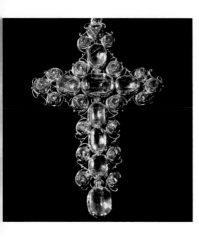

Gold cross with aquamarines and diamonds, 90 mm high, made in Bohemia, first half of 19th century.

Processing: faceted cuts, cabochons, engravings
Similar minerals: sapphire, topaz, spinel, apatite
Imitations: synthetic spinel, synthetic corundum, glass
Identification: hardness, specific gravity, optical methods
Care: Aquamarine is fragile and should be handled with care. There are no cleaning problems unless stone contains inclusions.

Aquamarine crystal, 127 mm long, Shigar, Pakistan.

Other large rough aquamarines from Brazil include the Martha Rocha (54 kg) and the Jaceto (18 kg). Madagascar (Bevoni region, Antsanatra, Betsinoba, Andotra) has also produced very fine gemmy, deep blue and green aquamarines. In the United States, aquamarines come from pegmatites in Colorado, Maine, and California (Pala district). In Russia, they come from the Ural Mts. and Transbaikalia, where an aquamarine crystal weighing 82 kg was found in 1796. Fine aquamarines also come from Ukraine. Other deposits are known from Zimbabwe (Bikita, Salisbury, Miami), Tanzania, Namibia, Mozambique, Kenya, South Africa, as well as from Sri Lanka, Burma, India, and (recently) Pakistan, Afghanistan, China, and Australia. European aquamarines are known from Ireland and Norway. Aquamarines were often cut and mounted in crown jewels, and a 920 ct. stone appears in the British imperial crown. Large cut stones from Brazil are in the National Museum in Prague (988 ct.) and the Natural History Museum in London (875 ct.). The world's largest cut aquamarine reportedly weighs 2,594 ct. and measures 146 x 47 x 38 mm. Many unique pieces are at the Smithsonian Institution in Washington, D.C., or the American Museum of Natural History in New York.

Heliodor
(beryl variety)

$Be_3Al_2Si_6O_{18}$

From Greek *helios* – "sun,"
hence "bright yellow"

Color: yellow with a greenish or honey tint, golden yellow, lemon yellow (*golden beryl*) • **Diaphaneity:** transparent, translucent • **Luster:** glassy • **Fracture:** conchoidal, uneven • **Cleavage:** indistinct • **Hardness:** 7.5–8, brittle • **Streak:** white • **Specific gravity:** 2.72 • **Refractive index:** N_e–1.566–1.584, N_o–1.570–1.591 • **Birefringence:** 0.005–0.009 • **Dispersion:** 0.014 • **Pleochroism:** weak • **Luminescence:** none • **Chemistry:** color caused by Fe^{3+} • **Special features:** chatoyancy, rare asterism • **Treatment:** heating, irradiation

History: Since its discovery in 1910, heliodor has been prized for its fine color and the high quality of its cut stones.
Astrology: birthstone for Leo
Chakra: navel
Healing effects: promotes digestion; discharge stone in running water, then recharge briefly in sunlight
Host rocks: pegmatites
Occurrences: The first reported heliodors, which contain trace amounts of uranium and are therefore slightly radioactive, were from Namibia, near Otavi and Roessing. Other African localities include Madagascar (Maharitra region), Zimbabwe, and Botswana. Crystals up to 7 cm were found near St. Anna in Zimbabwe in 1960, as well as in pegmatites near Miami, Bikita, and Salisbury. The most important source for gemmy heliodors is Brazil, in particular, Santa Maria do Sugau, Virgem da Lapa (Minas Gerais), and Veruga (Bahía), where crystals up to 70 cm long have been found. Deep brown beryls with a golden tint occur in Governador Valadares (Minas Gerais). In the United States, zonal colored heliodors are known from Maine (Mt. Mica). Crystals over 5 cm were found in India

Typical heliodor crystal with etching figures, 75 mm long, Volodarsk Volynskii, Ukraine.

(Orissa). Probably the best and the most beautiful heliodors come from the pegmatites of Ukraine (Volodarsk Volynskii near Zhitomir), where the largest gemmy crystal measured 35 x 15 cm. Heliodors also occur in Russia (Ural Mts. near Murzinka; Transbaikalia). Rare crystals are known from Sweden (Varuträsk), and very rare gemmy crystals, from the Czech Republic (Písek). Faceted cuts over 100 ct. are relatively common in many museum collections. The Smithsonian Institution in Washington, D.C., has a cut yellow stone weighing 133.5 ct. and a cat's–eye weighing 43.5 ct., while the Natural History Museum in London has a cut yellow stone weighing 82.25 ct. and a crystal weighing 4 kg (27 cm long) – all from Madagascar. The Royal Ontario Museum in Toronto has a faceted yellow heliodor weighing 78.8 ct.

Processing: faceted cuts, cabochons, carvings

Similar minerals: sapphire, topaz, cubic zirconia, chrysoberyl, citrine, brazilianite ·

Imitations: synthetic spinel, fianite, YAG, glass

Identification: hardness, specific gravity, optical methods

Care: Heliodor is fragile and should be handled with care. There are no cleaning problems unless stone contains inclusions.

Cut heliodors; largest, 21 ct., Volodarsk Volynskii, Ukraine.

Morganite
(beryl variety)

$Be_3Al_2Si_6O_{18}$

After J. P. Morgan

History: A rare variety of beryl, morganite has been known by that name since 1911. Beryl of the same color from Russia was named **vorobyevite** (after Russian mineralogist V. I. Vorobyev).
Astrology: birthstone for Libra
Chakra: heart
Healing effects: cleanses, strengthens heart; discharge stone in running water,

Color: pink, pink–red, purple • **Diaphaneity:** transparent, translucent • **Luster:** glassy • **Fracture:** conchoidal, uneven • **Cleavage:** indistinct • **Hardness:** 7.5–8 • **Streak:** white • **Specific gravity:** 2.71–2.90 • **Refractive index:** N_e –1.572, N_o–1.578–1.600 • **Birefringence:** 0.008–0.010 • **Dispersion:** 0.014 • **Pleochroism:** distinct • **Luminescence:** sometimes weak purple • **Chemistry:** color caused by trace amounts of Cs, Li, Mn • **Special features:** occasional chatoyancy • **Treatment:** heating, irradiation

then recharge briefly in sunlight
Host rocks: pegmatites, placers

Morganite crystals on matrix, 105 mm wide, Pala district, California.

Processing: faceted cuts, cabochons, carvings

Similar minerals: topaz, sapphire, spinel, kunzite

Imitations: synthetic spinel, cubic zirconia, YAG, glass, synthetic morganite, synthetic red beryl

Identification: hardness, specific gravity, optical methods

Care: Morganite is fragile and should be handled with care. Avoid excessive heat. Color fades in the daylight. There are no cleaning problems unless stone contains inclusions.

Morganite cut, 191.60 ct., White Queen Mine, Pala district, California.

Red beryl crystal, 17 mm long, Violet Claims, Wah Wah Mts., Utah.

Occurrences: Formally described from the Pala district in San Diego Co., California, and often associated with tourmaline, morganite is rare in the Ramona district of the same county, and is also known from Notway, Maine. Brazil has produced a significant number of morganites from different localities in Minas Gerais (Alto do Gis and others). Highly prized gemmy morganites with a distinct pink color occur in the Maharitra region of Madagascar, with cut stones exceeding 500 ct. A morganite goddess carving from the American Museum of Natural History measures 11. x 6 cm; the rough came from Anjanaboboina, Madagascar. St. Petersburg Museum in Russia has a cut stone weighing 598.7 ct. and a rough weighing 5 kg. The Smithsonian Institution in Washington, D.C., has cut stones ranging between 56 and 287 ct. The Royal Ontario Museum in Toronto has a stone weighing 118.6 ct. All of these come from either Madagascar or Brazil. Other important sources for morganite have included Mozambique (Alto Ligonha district), Zimbabwe, Namibia, China, Russia (Ural Mts.), Italy (Elba), and Kazakhstan. Red beryl, called *bixbite*, comes from the Violet Claims, Wah Wah Mts., Utah. Its faceted cuts do not exceed 10 ct.

Phenakite

Be_2SiO_4

From Greek *phenax* – "deceiver" because it was often mistaken for quartz

History: Formally described in 1833, phenakite has been very rarely used for jewelry purposes.
Host rocks: pegmatites, placers
Occurrences: Large crystals (up to 8 cm) are known from Habachtal, Austria, and from the Ural Mts., Russia (up to 18 cm). Yellow and light red crystals come from Brazil. Phenakite also occurs in the United States, Mexico, Sri Lanka (cut stone weighing 569 ct.), Burma, Tanzania, and Madagascar.
Processing: faceted cuts
Similar minerals: rock crystal, topaz, apatite
Imitations: synthetic phenakite

Color: colorless, yellow, pink, wine yellow, brown • **Diaphaneity:** transparent, translucent • **Luster:** glassy • **Fracture:** conchoidal • **Cleavage:** indistinct • **Hardness:** 7.5–8, brittle • **Streak:** white • **Specific gravity:** 2.93–3.00 • **Refractive index:** N_e–1.670, N_o–1.654 • **Birefringence:** 0.016 • **Dispersion:** 0.015 • **Pleochroism:** distinct – colorless, orange, yellow • **Luminescence:** sometimes light purple or pink • **Chemistry:** insoluble in acids • **Special features:** none • **Treatment:** not known

Identification: hardness, specific gravity, optical methods
Care: Ultrasonic and steam cleaning are relatively safe.

Cut phenakites from Malyshevo; largest, 10 ct., Ural Mts., Russia

Euclase

BeAlSiO₄(OH)

From Greek
u + klasis = "good–cleaving"

History: Formally described in 1792, euclase was not used as a gemstone until recently.
Host rocks: pegmatites
Occurrences: Abundant deposits of green and blue euclase occur in Brazil, with crystals up to 4 cm and unique cut stones up to 25 ct. It is also found in Zimbabwe (large crystals up to 8 cm), as well as in Uganda, the Democratic Republic of the Congo (Zaire), South Africa, Russia, Norway, and Austria.
Processing: faceted cuts, cabochons

Euclase crystal, 21 mm long, Hope Mine, Miami, Zimbabwe.

Color: colorless, greenish, blue • **Diaphaneity:** transparent, translucent • **Luster:** glassy to adamantine • **Fracture:** conchoidal • **Cleavage:** perfect • **Hardness:** 6.5–7.5 • **Streak:** white • **Specific gravity:** 3.0–3.1 • **Refractive index:** N_p–1.652, N_m–1.656, N_g–1.672 • **Birefringence:** 0.019–0.025 • **Dispersion:** 0.016 • **Pleochroism:** weak to strong – yellowish, blue, green • **Luminescence:** sometimes deep red, indistinct • **Chemistry:** color caused by Cr^{3+} • **Special features:** none • **Treatment:** not known

Similar minerals: aquamarine, hiddenite, topaz
Imitations: not known
Identification: specific gravity
Care: Protect euclase's perfect cleavage from sudden shocks and sudden temperature changes. Clean only in soap and water; do not use ultrasonic or steam cleaning.

Andalusite

Al_2SiO_5

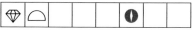

After Andalusia, Spain

Color: gray, red–gray, brown, pink, purple, blue; rarely green (**viridine**) • **Diaphaneity:** transparent to opaque • **Luster:** glassy • **Fracture:** even to uneven • **Cleavage:** good • **Hardness:** 6.5–7.5, brittle • **Refractive index:** N_p–1.629 –1.640, N_m–1.633–1.644, N_g–1.638 –1.650 • **Birefringence:** 0.007–0.011 • **Pleochroism:** distinct, strong – olive green, red • **Luminescence:** weak, green to yellow–green • **Chemistry:** color caused by trace amounts of Mn (viridine) • **Special features:** rare chatoyancy • **Treatment:** heating

History: Formally described in 1798.
Host rocks: metamorphic rocks, pegmatites, placers
Occurrences: Although a very common mineral, andalusite is rarely of gem quality. Some deposits are located in the Andalusia region of Spain. More important finds come from Brazil, where gemmy andalusite crystals reach 75–100 ct., and fine faceted stones are made from them. Placers in Minas Gerais and Espírito Santo have yielded brownish andalusites. Unique deep blue crystals are known from Burma and India. Andalusite has also been found in the gem–bearing gravels of Sri Lanka. The United States has produced andalusite from California, Maine, Connecticut, and New Mexico. Other localities include Canada (Quebec), Australia, and Tanzania (placers). Russian andalusites come from near Nerchinsk. Nice crystals up to 20 cm were recently found in Uzbekistan. Green andalusite crystals (viridine) occur in Sweden (Ultevis). Lower–quality material was found in Germany, the Czech Republic, and Austria, with rare blue andalusite crystals coming from Belgium. Large cut stones are very rare. The Smithsonian Institution in Washington, D.C., has a brown cut andalusite weighing 28.3 ct. and a green–brown cut stone weighing 13.5 ct., both from Brazil.
Processing: faceted cuts, cabochons
Similar minerals: verdelite, chrysoberyl
Imitations: glass
Identification: hardness, specific gravity, optical methods
Care: Protect andalusite from sudden shocks and sudden temperature changes. There are no cleaning problems unless stone contains inclusions.

Brilliant cut andalusites, 4 mm.

Chiastolite

(andalusite variety)

Al₂SiO₅

From Greek *chiastos* + *lithos*
= "cross stone" for crystal shape

History: The characteristic cross–shaped crystals of chiastolite, formally described in 1800, have long made it a natural choice for amulets.

Host rocks: metamorphic rocks

Occurrences: Chiastolite is known from Germany (Fichtelgebirge), Spain (Santiago do Compostella), and France (Bretagne, French Pyrenees). It is rare in the United Kingdom. Russian chiastolite comes from Transbaikalia. Nice chiastolites were found in Algeria (near Bona) and in Arizona, although the nicest occur in Australia (Bimbowrie region). High–quality stones have recently been discovered in China.

Processing: cabochons, slices; also used in natural shape (specimens)

Cut and polished chiastolite slices, slightly enlarged, from China (upper two) and from Bimbowrie, Australia (lower four).

Color: gray, brown • **Diaphaneity:** opaque • **Luster:** glassy • **Fracture:** even to uneven • **Cleavage:** good • **Hardness:** 6.5–7.5, brittle • **Streak:** white • **Specific gravity:** 3.13–3.17 • **Refractive index:** N_p–1.629–1.640, N_m–1.633–1.644, N_g–1.638–1.650 • **Birefringence:** 0.007–0.011 • **Pleochroism** strong, distinct – olive green, red • **Luminescence:** weak, green to yellow–green • **Chemistry:** color caused by Mn • **Special features:** none • **Treatment:** not known

Similar minerals: none

Imitations: glass

Identification: hardness, typical cross pattern

Care: Protect chiastolite from sudden shocks and sudden temperature changes. There are no cleaning problems unless stone contains inclusions.

Zircon

ZrSiO₄

After chemical
composition

History: Mentioned by Theophrastos (376–287 B.C.), and highly fashionable in the 15th and 16th centuries, zircon has been known through the ages. Especially prized were the jargon and hyacinth varieties, the latter as a talisman against pain and poisons (according to Aristotle). A stone of wisdom in the Middle Ages, zircon was believed to protect people from nightmares and evil ghosts.

Astrology: birthstone for Aquarius

Chakra: forehead

Healing effects: whets appetite; slakes thirst; strengthens nerves; used to treat ailments of lungs, liver, pancreas; discharge stone in running water, then recharge briefly in sunlight

Host rocks: igneous rocks, pegmatites, placers

Occurrences: Although very common, zircon only rarely occurs in large gemmy crystals. These are known from Renfrew, On-

Color: colorless (*Matura diamond*), yellow (*jargon*), red, orange–red (*hyacinth*), green, blue (*starlite*), brown, black • **Diaphaneity:** transparent, translucent • **Luster:** glassy, adamantine, greasy • **Fracture:** conchoidal • **Cleavage:** indistinct • **Hardness:** 6.5–7.5, brittle • **Streak:** white • **Specific gravity:** 3.9–4.8 • **Refractive index:** N_e–1.78 –2,01, N_o–1.81–1.97 • **Birefringence:** 0.059 (green has none) • **Dispersion:** 0.039 • **Pleochroism:** distinct (especially blue stones) • **Luminescence:** yellow, orange, green–yellow, sometimes none • **Chemistry:** color caused by Y, Nb, V, lanthanides • **Special features:** occasional slight radioactivity, rare chatoyancy • **Treatment:** heating (oxidation or reduction)

tario, Canada (crystals up to 7 kg), and Miass, Ural Mts., Russia (crystals up to 3.5 kg). Gemmy zircons of all the colors come from Sri Lanka (Ratnapura and Matara regions). Golden yellow and blue zircons are known from Thailand (Kha region). Fine jargons, some chatoyant, come from Aus-

Zircon pebbles of different colors, 10 mm, Sri Lanka.

Faceted zircons, 1.92 and 2.45 ct.

tralia (Anakia region) and from Burma (Mogok region). Similar material has been found in Vietnam, Cambodia, Thailand, and Burma. Red hyacinths occur in Russia (Ural Mts.), Madagascar, and France. Yellow and yellow–brown hyacinths come from Australia (Harts Range), South Africa, Tanzania, and Brazil. Natural starlites are very rare. Most commercial stones are hyacinths heat–treated to 800–1,000 °C, whose color may fade in sunlight. Natural starlites occur in Thailand (Kha region), Cambodia, and Sri Lanka. The best and most beautiful cut stones are at the Smithsonian Institution in Washington, D.C., including a brown stone from Sri Lanka (118.1 ct.), a red–brown from Burma (75.8 ct.), a brown from Thailand (64.2 ct.), and a green from Sri Lanka (23.5 ct.), as well as a blue cut stone from Thailand (103.2 ct.). The American Museum of Natural History in New York has a green–blue cut stone weighing 208 ct. from Sri Lanka, while the Royal Ontario Museum in Toronto has blue cut zircons weighing 61.69 ct., 63 ct., and 17.8 ct.

Processing: faceted cuts, cabochons
Similar minerals: sapphire, aquamarine, topaz, sinhalite, titanite
Imitations: synthetic spinel, synthetic rutile, glass, cubic zirconia
Identification: hardness, specific gravity, optical methods
Care: Clean zircon only in soap and water; do not use ultrasonic or steam cleaning. Some stones may fade when exposed to heat or sunlight.

Brilliant cut zircons; larger stone, 9 ct., Mir Pipe, Mironovo, Yakutia, Russia.

Garnet

$A_3B_2(SiO_4)_3$
A^{2+} = Mg, Fe, Ca, Mn
B^{3+} = Al, Fe, Cr, Ti, Zr, V
From French (*pomme*)
grenate – "pomegranate,"
hence "dark red"

History: Garnet has been long a favorite gemstone. Garnet jewelry is known from the Scythian period (6th–4th centuries B.C.). Pliny called all red gemstones, including garnet, *carbunculi*. Most favored was pyrope, often cut in Bohemia in the 16th century and used against witches' spells. Almandine was called *carbunculus alabandicus* by Pliny. Garnet was believed to protect its owner from enemies, to stimulate the imagination, and to advance the cause of love.

Color: red (*pyrope*), brown–red (*spessartine, andradite*), purple–red (*almandine, rhodolite*), pink (rhodolite), green (*grossular*, andradite, *uvarovite*), yellow–green (grossular), black–brown, black (*melanite*), colorless (grossular) • **Diaphaneity:** transparent, translucent • **Luster:** glassy, silky • **Fracture:** conchoidal • **Cleavage:** none • **Hardness:** 6.5–7.5, brittle • **Streak:** white • **Refractive index / Specific gravity:** pyrope (rhodolite) N–1.730–1.766 / 3.79–3.89, almandine N–1.750–1.830 / 3.95–4.30, grossular (*hessonite, tsavorite, rosolite*), N–1.720–1.800 / 3.40–3.71; andradite (*demantoid, topazolite*, melanite), N–1.880–1.940 / 3.70–4.10; uvarovite, N–1.74–1.87 / 3.40–3.80; spessartine, N–1.790–1.810 / 3.80–4.25 • **Birefringence:** none • **Dispersion:** 0.022–0.057 • **Pleochroism:** none • **Luminescence:** none • **Chemistry:** color caused by trace amounts of Cr^{3+}, Fe^{3+} • **Special features:** asterism, chatoyancy, alexandrite effect • **Treatment:** not known

Characteristic almandine crystal, 50 mm, Russell, Massachusetts.

Astrology: birthstone for Aries, Leo (Greeks)
Chakra: base
Healing effects: revitalizes; builds blood, regulates blood pressure; used to treat arthritis, rheumatism, also mental disorders, as well as to increase sexual potency; discharge stone in running water, then dip into strong salt solution and recharge briefly in sunlight
Host rocks: igneous and metamorphic rocks, placers, pegmatites
Occurrences: Pyrope has long been mined and cut in Bohemia (**Bohemian garnet**), where pyrope–bearing placers cover about 70 km² (27 mi²). Slightly larger stones come from Cape Province, South Africa (**Cape rubies**). Pyrope is also known from Russia (Yakutia, associated with diamonds) and from the United States (Arkansas, Arizona, Colorado, New Mexico, and Utah). The most famous U.S. pyrope

Grossular crystal, 17 mm. Jeffrey Mine, Asbestos, Quebec, Canada.

comes from Arkansas (**Arkansas ruby**). Pyope has been described from Brazil, Argentina, Australia (Anakia region), Tanzania (rough stone up to 25 g), Zaire, Zimbabwe, and Mongolia (Shavarin–Caram region). Large pyrope accumulations have recently been found in Nigeria (Panyam region). Rhodolite garnet, a variety between pyrope and almandine, occurs in Sri Lanka, Zimbabwe, Kenya, and Tanzania. The most common garnet species is almandine, found principally in southern India and Sri Lanka. Good–quality crystals come also from Mongolia (Altan–Khuduk), Brazil (Minas Gerais), the United States (New York; Wrangell Island, Alaska), Madagascar, Austria, the Czech Republic, Norway, and Russia. Grossular occurs in Sri Lanka, Russia (Vilyui River basin), Tanzania (the Umba River basin), Kenya, Mexico, and the United States (California, Washington). It is known from South Africa under the name **Transvaal jade**. Brown–red romanzovites come from Finland. Brown hessonites occur in the Czech Republic, Russia, and Spain. Emerald green tsavorites (crystals up to 5 cm)

occur chiefly in the Tsavo National Park in Tanzania, but also in Kenya and Uzbekistan. Garnets of almost all colors (yellow, brown, orange, green) most recently come from Mali. Gemmy andradites are mined

Andradite, 14 mm, Sonora, Mexico.

in Mexico (crystals up to 1 cm). Andradite crystals have been found also on Seriphos Island, Greece, and in skarns of the Prince of Wales Island, Alaska (crystals up to 7 cm). Many localities in Russia have produced fine garnets (Kola Peninsula). Black, opaque melanites come from Germany, Italy, and France. Very fine green demantoids were found in chromite deposits in Russia (Sarany, Ural Mts.), in Italy (Val Malenco), the United States (Arizona), and elsewhere. Very rare topazolites occur in Russia (Ural Mts.) and Italy (Val Malenco), with bronze brown crystals up to 5 cm known from Arizona. Olive green crystals come from California and Switzerland and are quite common in Sri Lankan placers. Uvarovite, a rare member of the garnet group and usually associated with chromite, is found chiefly in the Ural Mts., Russia (very rare crystals up to 1 cm). Fine crystals are also known from Finland (Outokumpu), Turkey, Iran, South Africa, Ethiopia, and the United States (Oregon). Spessartine garnet is fairly common, but gemmy crystals are very rare. Very fine large spessartines (crystals up to 2 cm)

*Assorted colors of **grossular–andradite** garnet, largest, 5 ct., Diakon, Mali.*

have recently been found in the Gilgit region of Pakistan. They also come from Sri Lanka, Brazil, the United States, Mexico, Tanzania (crystals up to 5 cm), Kenya, and Greece (Seriphos Island – crystals up to 1 cm). Major museum collections have many large fine cut garnets. The Smithsonian Institution in Washington, D.C. has cut almandines from Idaho (174 and 67.3 ct.), a cut grossular from Sri Lanka (64.2 ct.), a cut andradite from Russia (10.4 ct.), a cut rhodolite from Tanzania (74.3 ct.), and a cut spessartine from Brazil (109 ct.). The largest cut pyrope has been reported from the Czech Republic (633.4 ct.). The largest cut pyrope in the garnet jewelry of Ulrike von Loewetzow also comes from the Czech Republic (13.2 ct.). The largest cut tsavorite weighs more than 20 ct., while cut topazolites over 1 ct. are extremely rare.

Processing: faceted cuts, cabochons, engravings

mandine, Stikine
iver, Wrangell,
aska.

imilar minerals: spinel, ruby, emerald, ve-uvianite, chrome diopside
nitations: spinel, glass, YAG, synthetic co-undum

Identification: hardness, specific gravity, optical methods
Care: Protect garnet from sudden temperature changes. Clean in soap and water; do not use steam cleaning.

*ut garnets (from the left): rhodolite, 10.5 ct.;
avorite, 3.39 ct.; spessartine, 16.45 ct.*

Tourmaline

$WX_3Y_6(BO_3)_3Si_6O_{18}(O,OH,F)_4$
$W^+ = Na$
$X^{2+} = Fe, Mg, Ca, Mn, (Li + Al)$
$Y^{3+} = Al, Fe$

From Sinhalese
toramelli – "carnelian"

History: Dutch sailors first brought tourmaline, then called *toramelli*, from Sri Lanka to Europe in 1703. The rubellite variety has been used as a gemstone ever since. Because of its electric properties, tourmaline has often been used to transfer energy. It was believed to stimulate artistic abilities and soon became a spiritual stone.

Elbaite crystal on albite, 45 mm long, Lavra do Cruzeiro, Minas Gerais, Brazil.

Color: colorless (*achroite*), pink (*rubellite*), blue (*indicolite, dravite, schorl*), green (*verdelite, uvite,* dravite), yellow (*elbaite, Mn–rich tourmaline*), brown, yellow–brown (dravite, *buergerite*), black (schorl, uvite, buergerite), multicolored (elbaite, *liddicoatite*) • **Diaphaneity:** transparent to opaque • **Luster:** glassy • **Fracture:** uneven, conchoidal • **Cleavage:** poor • **Hardness:** 7–7.5 • **Streak:** white • **Specific gravity:** 3.02–3.41 • **Refractive index / Birefringence:** elbaite (achroite, indicolite, rubellite, verdelite), N_e–1.615–1.620, N_o–1.640–1.655 / 0.025–0.035; dravite, N_e–1.610–1.632, N_o–1.635–1.661 / 0.021–0.026; schorl, N_e–1.625–1.650, N_o–1.655–1.675 / 0.025–0.035; liddicoatite, N_e–1.621, N_o–1.637 / 0.016; Mn–rich tourmaline N_e–1.622–1.623, N_o–1.645–1.648 / 0.023–0–028; uvite N_e–1.612–1.639, N_o–1.632–1.660 / 0.017–0–021; buergerite, N_e–1.655–1.670, N_o–1.735 / 0.065–0.080 • **Dispersion:** 0.017 • **Pleochroism:** strong dichroism • **Luminescence:** sometimes yellow (dravite), green, blue (elbaite, liddicoatite), dark purple (achroite), none (schorl) • **Chemistry:** intense color caused by Li, Mn, Cr; intensifies further at temperatures from 150 to 650°C • **Special features:** chatoyancy, color zoning, rare alexandrite effect • **Treatment:** irradiation, heating

Astrology: birthstone for Pisces
Chakra: heart
Healing effects: improves memory; prevents vertigo; discharge stone in water, then recharge briefly in sunlight
Host rocks: pegmatites, metamorphic rocks, igneous rocks, placers
Occurrences: Some of the world's largest and best elbaite crystals come from Brazilian pegmatites, chiefly in Minas Gerais. Crystals up to 1 m long were found in Itatiaia in 1978 (Rocket, Rose of Itatiaia). One very nice gemmy, dark red crystal measured 25 x 11 cm (Flower of Brazil). The Virgem da Lapa region has produced

multicolored elbaites. Named after Elba Island, Italy, elbaite is also found in Moravia, Czech Republic (Řečice, Strážek), and multicolored elbaites are known from Connecticut. Santa Rosa and Morro Redondo, Brazil, have been good sources for the popular **watermelon tourmaline** (crystals with a pink core and a green rim), although it also occurs in the United States. A large druse of rubellite crystals up to 40 cm long, weighing 4 t (4.4 short tons) was also reported from Brazil. Very fine rubellites have been known from many pegmatites in the United States (Maine, California). Californian tourmalines come mostly from the Pala and Mesa Grande districts, San Diego Co. A rubellite druse measuring 32 x 27 cm, found there in 1969, is preserved at the Smithsonian Institution in Washington, D.C. The Himalaya Mine in the Mesa Grande district is the biggest single tourmaline producer in the world. Afghanistan (Nuristan region), Mozambique (Alta Ligonha district), Madagascar, and Zambia have recently become important tourmaline producers, as well. Nice pink Russian tourmalines have been known from the Ural Mts. (local name **sibirite**) and from Transbaikalia. Nice blue Brazilian indi-

Elbaite crystal on quartz, 32 mm, Minas Gerais, Brazil.

colites, with crystals up to 10 cm long, are known from Morro Redondo. Indicolite is also known from the United States (California, Maine), and very rare indicolites were found in Madagascar (Betafo region) and Namibia (Klein Spitzkopje). Dark blue dravites from China are rare. Almost always associated with rubellites and indicolites, very nice verdelite crystals up to 10 cm are known from Minas Gerais, Brazil. An extraordinary crystal, 1 m long and 20 cm thick, called the Rocket, was found in Itatiaia. Other crystals have weighed up to 4 kg. In the United States, verdelite comes from Maine, California, and Connecticut. One of the best specimens, the Jolly Green Giant, measures 27 x 10 cm and is preserved in the American Museum of Natural History in New York. Verdelites have also been found in Mozambique (Alta Ligonha district), Zambia, and Tanzania. Green dravites are known from Zimbabwe. Very nice green tourmalines were recently found in Pakistan and Afghanistan. European occurrences are in the Czech Republic (Bohemia, Moravia) and Italy (Elba). Achroite, a very rare variety of elbaite, has been found in Madagascar, Brazil, the United States (California), Elba and Afghanistan. Yellow and cinnamon yellow dravites come from Sri Lanka (**Ceylon olivines**). Red–brown dravites come from Kenya and emerald–green ones come from Tanzania. Brown isometric dravite crystals up to 15 cm occur in Western Australia (Yinniethara). Dravites are also known from Tajikistan (Pamir Mts.) and Russia (Ural Mts.). Yellow and brown Mn–rich tourmalines are very rare in the pegmatites of

...ut elbaite, 6.44 ct., Mt. Mica, Paris, Maine.

...epal and Mozambique. Sometimes used in ...neral jewelry, black schorls are fairly com-...on as large crystals in Brazil, the United ...tates (California, Maine, Connecticut), Na-...ibia, Kazakhstan (crystals over I m long), ...kraine, Norway (crystals measuring up to ...x I m), and the Czech Republic. Liddicoatite ...ccurs in Madagascar as multicolored crys-...ls, up to 50 cm long and zonally perpen-...cular to the c–axis. Many major museums ...ave significant tourmalines in their collec-...ons. The Smithsonian Institution in Wash-...gton, D.C., has several cut elbaites, weigh-...g from 17.7 ct. to 246 ct., from Brazil, the

United States, and Mozambique. A unique cut rubellite weighing 255 ct. is preserved in Moscow's Diamond Fund. Originally thought to be a ruby, this stone used to be a part of the collection of Rudolf II in Prague and probably comes from Burma.

Processing: faceted cuts, cabochons, engravings, carvings

Similar minerals: amethyst, chrysoberyl, olivine, ruby, emerald, sapphire, topaz, zircon, spinel, vesuvianite

Imitations: glass

Identification: hardness, specific gravity, optical methods

Care: Clean tourmaline in soap and water only; do not use ultrasonic or steam cleaning. Multicolored stones are fragile on the color boundaries and should be handled carefully.

...ut elbaites, 24.66 and 18.22 ct.

Cordierite

$Mg_2Al_4Si_5O_{18}$

After P. L. Cordier

History: The Vikings were said to have used cordierite in navigating; thanks to the stone's strong pleochroism, they could follow the sun even under cloudy skies.

Host rocks: pegmatites, metamorphic rocks, placers

Occurrences: Common as a mineral, cordierite only rarely occurs as a gemstone (iolite). Gemmy crystals have been found in Brazil, Sri Lanka, India (Tamil Nadu), Madagascar, Tanzania, Namibia, and the United States (Wyoming, California, Connecticut). It is also known from Russia (Ural Mts., Kola Peninsula) and Tajikistan (Pamir Mts.). Crystals up to 20 cm were found in Sweden, Finland, and Spain. The largest stone, cut in the shape of a crystal and weighing 885 ct., is preserved in the Natural History Museum in London.

Processing: faceted cuts, cabochons

Color: blue, green–blue, gray, purple, gray–brown • **Diaphaneity:** transparent, translucent • **Luster:** glassy • **Fracture:** conchoidal • **Cleavage:** good • **Hardness:** 7–7.5, brittle • **Streak:** white • **Specific gravity:** 2.53–2.78 • **Refractive index:** N_p–1.522–1.558, N_m–1.524–1.574, N_g–1.527–1.578 • **Birefringence:** 0.005–0.018 • **Dispersion:** 0.017 • **Pleochroism:** very strong – deep purple to light blue – strong trichroism visible to naked eye • **Luminescence:** none • **Chemistry:** stable in acids • **Special features:** chatoyancy, aventurescence • **Treatment:** not known

Similar minerals: sapphire, aquamarine
Identification: specific gravity, optical method
Care: Protect cordierite (iolite) from sudden shocks and sudden temperature changes. Clean in soap and water only; do not use ultrasonic or steam cleaning.

Cordierite cube with distinct pleochroism, 10 mm, Madagascar.

Kornerupine

$Mg_4(Al,Fe^{3+})_6(Si,B)_4O_{21}(OH)$

After A. N. Kornerup

History: Formally described in 1884.
Host rocks: metamorphic rocks, placers
Occurrences: Kornerupine is a rare mineral. Gem–quality deep green to brown–green stones occur in Sri Lanka near Matara. Nice kornerupines also come from Burma and Madagascar. Apple green stones come from Kenya, and dark green ones from South Africa, Canada, and Greenland. Rare crystals up to 20 cm have been found in Greenland. Kornerupine occurs in Russia and Finland, as well. Chatoyant and rare faceted stones are of interest to collectors.
Processing: faceted cuts, cabochons
Similar minerals: andalusite

Cut kornerupine, 5 mm.

Color: colorless, brown–yellow, pink, green, blue–green, brown, black • **Diaphaneity:** transparent to translucent, opaque • **Luster:** glassy • **Fracture:** conchoidal • **Cleavage:** perfect • **Hardness:** 6–7 • **Streak:** white • **Specific gravity:** 3.28–3.45 • **Refractive index:** N_p–1.660–1.682, N_m–1.674–1.696, N_g–1.675–1.699 • **Birefringence:** 0.013–0.017 • **Dispersion:** 0.018 • **Pleochroism:** strong, visible to naked eye – yellow to green, light green to brown–green, colorless • **Luminescence:** very rare yellowish • **Chemistry:** soluble in HF • **Special features:** chatoyancy, rare asterism • **Treatment:** not known

Imitations: none
Identification: optical methods
Care: Protect kornerupine's perfect cleavage from sudden shocks and sudden temperature changes. Clean in soap and water only; do not use ultrasonic or steam cleaning.

Rock crystal
(quartz variety)

SiO_2

From Greek
krystallos – "ice, crystal"

History: Known already in Mesolithic times (12th to 8th millennium B.C.), rock crystal was sold as petrified ice by the Romans. Theophrastos called it *krystallos*, and Pliny also mentioned it. The name "quartz" came from Agricola (1529). Eastern civilizations considered quartz a stone of patience and perfection, and it was used as a cure for wounds in Tibet. Crystal balls are made of quartz and have been used for magical purposes. Drinking from rock crystal glasses was believed to prevent toothaches. It is one of the seven preciousnesses for Buddhists.

Astrology: birthstone for Capricorn
Chakra: crown

Color: colorless; sometimes slightly milky white • **Diaphaneity:** transparent • **Luster:** glassy • **Fracture:** conchoidal, uneven • **Cleavage:** indistinct or none • **Hardness:** 7, brittle • **Streak:** white • **Specific gravity:** 2.65 • **Refractive index:** N_e–1.553, N_o–1.544 • **Birefringence:** 0.009 • **Dispersion:** 0.013 • **Pleochroism:** none • **Luminescence:** none • **Chemistry:** soluble in HF • **Special features:** iridescence, aventurescence • **Treatment:** not known

Cut rock crystals, used for healing; pyramid is 110 mm high.

Rock crystal engraving, 35 mm high, carved by Eva Vîšková, Pardubice, Czech Republic.

Healing effects: revitalizes body; neutralizes radiation; slakes thirst; used to treat ailments of stomach, heart; discharge stone in water, then recharge briefly in sunlight

Host rocks: igneous rocks, pegmatites, hydrothermal and alpine–type veins, placers

Occurrences: Although a very common mineral, rock crystal is not always of gem quality. India and Sri Lanka·(near Tatnaputi) were historically important producers. Iridescent crystals from Poona (India) and Burma are very rare. Nice crystals come from Kenya, Madagascar, French Guiana, and Brazil (Minas Gerais, Goiás, Bahía). Many rock crystal localities are in the United States (pegmatites – Auburn, Maine; New Jersey; North Carolina; Crystal Peak, Arkansas; California; and elsewhere). At present, it is mined in some Russian deposits (Polar

Urals, Yuzhnyi) and also produced in Ukraine, Kazakhstan, and Georgia. The Alpine localities are very important, as well. Rock crystal is found in Switzerland (canton Uri – 135 kg crystal; St. Gotthard; Grimsel; and other places), Austria (Grossglockner – a crystal weighing 1 t, found in 1965) and Italy. Rock crystal also comes from Germany, the Czech Republic, Poland, and France (Dauphiné). Rare bipyramidal crystals from the Maramures region in Romania are called "**Marmarosh diamonds**". Usually small, they are nonetheless useful in their natural shape for jewelry. Similar material is known from Ukraine, Slovakia, and the United States. Stones called "**Herkimer diamonds**" are found in Herkimer Co., New York. Many unique cut rock crystals are in museums all over the world. The Smithsonian Institution in Washington, D.C., has a faceted stone weighing 7,000 ct. and a rock crystal ball, 33 cm in diameter, weighing 48.5 kg (rough material came from Burma and was cut in China).

Processing: faceted cuts, cabochons, engravings, carvings

Similar minerals: diamond, topaz, danburite, zircon, achroite

Imitations: glass, synthetic quartz

Identification: hardness, specific gravity, optical methods

Care: Rock crystal may crack at high temperatures. Ultrasonic cleaning is recommended.

Rock crystal druse, 95 mm high, Arkansas.

Citrine
(quartz variety)

SiO$_2$

from Latin *citrus* – "citron,"
hence "lemon yellon"

History: Amethyst annealing produced citrines already in the Middle Ages.
Astrology: birthstone for Gemini
Chakra: navel
Healing effects: promotes digestion, healthy functioning of liver, pancreas; discharge stone in water, then recharge briefly in sunlight
Host rocks: igneous rocks, pegmatites, hydrothermal and alpine–type veins, placers
Occurrences: Natural citrines are rare. Brazil is an important producer of citrine (Cristallina and Aragua, Goiás; Bahía; and Minas Gerais). Citrine comes also from the United States (Pikes Peak, Colorado; New Hampshire; North Carolina), and Madagascar, where it is associated with rock crystal and smoky quartz (Vohémar

Ametrine carving, 48 mm wide, Bolivian stone, carved by Suzan Alenn, United States.

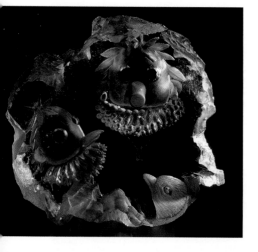

Color: yellow, yellow–brown, lemon yellow, yellow–orange • **Diaphaneity:** transparent, translucent • **Luster:** glassy • **Fracture:** conchoidal, uneven • **Cleavage:** indistinct or none • **Hardness:** 7, brittle • **Streak:** white • **Specific gravity:** 2.65 • **Refractive index:** N$_e$–1.553, N$_o$–1.544 • **Birefringence:** 0.009 • **Dispersion:** 0.013 • **Pleochroism:** weak in natural stones, synthetic stones have none • **Luminescence:** none • **Chemistry:** color caused by Fe^{3+}, Al, Li; fades at 200 °C, 300 °C, and 560 °C, respectively; other quartz varieties turn yellow (artificial citrine) • **Special features:** iridescence, chatoyancy • **Treatment:** heating, irradiation

Druse of citrine crystals, product of amethyst annealing, Brazil.

and Mahanoro regions). Other localities are known from Russia (near Murzinka, Ural Mts.) and Kazakhstan. Rare European citrines have been found in the Czech Republic (near Velké Meziříčí), Spain (near Córdoba and Salamanca), France (Dauphiné), and Scotland (Arran Island). Large citrine crystals are very rare. The Smithsonian Institution in Washington, D.C., has several cut citrines from Brazil, weighing 2,258 ct., 1,180 ct., and 783 ct.
Processing: faceted cuts, cabochons, engravings, carvings

Citrine crystals, Khasavarka, Russia; cut synthetic citrine, 58 ct., Russia.

Different–colored citrines from different localities; largest, 52 ct., is from Brazil.

Similar minerals: topaz, orthoclase, zircon (hyacinth)
Imitations: glass, synthetic quartz
Identification: hardness, optical methods
Care: Ultrasonic cleaning is recommended.

Smoky quartz
(quartz variety)

SiO₂

Color: light brown, gray–brown, brown, brown–black; black variety is called *morion* • **Diaphaneity:** transparent to translucent, opaque • **Luster:** glassy • **Fracture:** conchoidal, uneven • **Cleavage:** indistinct or none • **Hardness:** 7, brittle • **Streak:** white • **Specific gravity:** 2.65 • **Refractive index:** N_e–1.553, N_o–1.544 • **Birefringence:** 0.009 • **Dispersion:** 0.013 • **Pleochroism:** visible only in dark–colored stones • **Luminescence:** usually none • **Chemistry:** color caused by Al, Li, Na; changes with rising temperature • **Special features:** iridescence, chatoyancy • **Treatment:** heating, irradiation

History: Smoky quartz has long been used in jewelry, often in gentlemen's rings, and for making lapidary objects.

Astrology: birthstone for Capricorn

Chakra: secondary center in hands

Healing effects: relieves pain, also depression; used to treat nervous disorders; discharge stone in water, then recharge briefly in sunlight

Host rocks: pegmatites, metamorphic rocks, placers

Occurrences: Brazil is the world's most important producer of druses and crystals of smoky quartz, with many localities in Minas Gerais, São Paulo, Goiás. Good smoky quartz also comes from the United States (Auburn, Maine – crystals up to 200 kg; Arkansas; Caroll Co., New Hampshire; Pikes Peak, Colorado; Texas; Montana; Utah; San Diego Co., California; North Carolina). Most occurrences in Africa are located in Mozambique (Alta Ligonha district) and

Different–colored cut smoky quartzes; largest, 180 ct., is from Austrian Alps.

Faceted quartzes with sharp boundary between rock crystal and smoky quartz; larger stone weighs 40 ct., Volodarsk Volynskii, Ukraine.

Madagascar (Vohémar and Mahanoro regions). Smoky quartz is also known from Japan and Australia (New South Wales). Very important finds were made in Russia

Druse of smoky quartz crystals, 110 mm high, Polar Urals, Russia.

(Ural Mts.), Ukraine (Volodarsk Volynskii), and Kazakhstan. Large crystals were often found in Maine pegmatites in the United States – the largest crystal was 117.5 cm long and 42.5 cm thick and weighed 230 kg. A very large smoky quartz crystal of a lesser quality weighing 40 t (44 short tons) was discovered in Brazil. The largest known crystal comes from Kazakhstan, measuring 7.5 x 1.6 m and weighing about 70 t (77 short tons). Smoky quartz has been found in Europe, too. Scotland (Cairngorn region), Austria (near Sulzbachtal), and Switzerland (St. Gotthard, Galenstock, Uri) are among the most important localities. Finds in other European countries (Czech Republic, Germany, Poland, and Spain) are less important. Cut smoky quartzes are common. A very large cut stone (4,500 ct.) is at the Smithsonian Institution in Washington, D.C.

Processing: faceted cuts, cabochons, carvings, engravings

Similar minerals: topaz, andalusite, axinite, dravite, sanidine

Imitations: glass, synthetic smoky quartz

Identification: hardness, specific gravity, optical methods

Care: Ultrasonic cleaning is recommended.

Rose quartz

(quartz variety)

SiO_2

History: Rose quartz has been used as a gemstone since earliest history.
Astrology: birthstone for Taurus
Chakra: heart
Healing effects: relieves depression; strengthens heart; discharge stone in water, then recharge briefly in sunlight
Host rocks: pegmatites

Color: light pink, pink, pink–red • **Diaphaneity:** transparent to translucent, milky • **Luster:** glassy, greasy • **Fracture:** conchoidal, uneven • **Cleavage:** indistinct or none • **Hardness:** 7, brittle • **Streak:** white • **Specific gravity:** 2.65 • **Refractive index:** N_e–1.553, N_o–1.544 • **Birefringence:** 0.009 • **Dispersion:** 0.013 • **Pleochroism:** distinct in pink varieties • **Luminescence:** none • **Chemistry:** color caused by Ti • **Special features:** occasional asterism or chatoyancy • **Treatment:** not known

Rose quartz from different localities; cut stones, about 10 ct..

Occurrences: The best–quality rose quartz is mined in Madagascar, with big blocks known from Vahinancaratra and Ambositra. Rose quartz cat's–eyes come from gem–bearing gravels in Sri Lanka. Other localities are in Kenya, Mozambique, and Namibia (Roessing). Many rose quartz deposits are in Brazil (Jequitinhonha, Aracuai, Governador Valadares, San Miguel), and the world's first rose quartz crystals were found in Sapucaia (Minas Gerais) in 1959. Brazil has also produced some stones with chatoyancy and asterism. In the United States, rose quartz occurs in Maine, California, South Dakota, and Colorado. Star rose quartz is known from New York and Georgia. Rose quartz comes from Russia (Ural Mts. Karelia), Kazakhstan, India, and Japan, as well. The Czech Republic (Dolní Bory, Písek), Germany, Switzerland, Finland, and other countries in Europe have also produced rose quartz. Faceted cut stones over 20 ct. are rare. The American Museum of Natural History in New York has a chatoyant rose quartz ball weighing 625 ct.
Processing: faceted cuts, cabochons, engravings, carvings
Similar minerals: morganite
Imitations: glass
Identification: hardness, specific gravity, optical methods
Care: Do not expose rose quartz to heat or direct sunlight. Clean in soap and water or with ultrasonic; do not use steam cleaning.

Rose quartz crystal, 80 mm high, Sapucaia, Minas Gerais, Brazil.

Amethyst
(quartz variety)

SiO$_2$

From Greek *amethystos*
– "remedy against drunkenness"

Color: light to dark purple, purple–red • **Diaphaneity:** transparent, translucent • **Luster:** glassy • **Fracture:** conchoidal, uneven • **Cleavage:** indistinct or none • **Hardness:** 7, brittle • **Streak:** white • **Specific gravity:** 2.63–2.65 • **Refractive index:** N_e–1.553, N_o–1.544 • **Birefringence:** 0.009 • **Dispersion:** 0.013 • **Pleochroism:** mostly weak, sometimes visible to naked eye • **Luminescence:** none • **Chemistry:** color caused by trace amounts of Fe^{2+}, Fe^{3+} • **Special features:** none • **Treatment:** heating, irradiation

History: The most beautiful of all quartz varieties, amethyst was known to the ancient Egyptians, Etruscans, and Romans. Small amethyst cameos were made in ancient China. Long a symbol of carnal love, it was called the "bishop's stone" in Europe during the Middle Ages and believed to protect its owner from witchcraft. According to legend, those who drank from amethyst cups could not become intoxicated.

Astrology: birthstone for Capricorn, Aries (Babylonians)

Chakra: crown

Healing effects: strengthens will; balances metabolism; used to treat neuralgia, also insomnia; discharge stone in running water, then recharge briefly in sunlight

Druse of amethyst crystals, 20 mm wide, Las Vigas, Veracruz, Mexico.

Palisade amethyst, *Bochovice, Czech Republic.*

Host rocks: metamorphic rocks, hydrothermal veins, placers

Occurrences: Brazil has been famous as an amethyst producer since the Middle Ages. Brazilian amethyst occurs as a lining of cavities in basaltic rocks over an area of about 1.5 million km^2 (580,000 mi^2), south into Uruguay. An enormous cavity, measuring 10 x 2 x 1 m, was found in 1900. Amethyst occurs in Bahía, Matto Grosso, Minas Gerais. Ametrine, a variety with yellow and purple zones, is found in Bolivia, next to the Brazilian border. Amethyst is mined also in the United States (Montana, Maine, Georgia, Arizona). It occurs in Canada (Thunder Bay region), Mexico, Bolivia, Sri Lanka, India (Deccan Plateau), Burma,

apan, China, and Korea. Madagascar is a
ery important amethyst producer, as are
Zimbabwe, Mozambique, the Democratic
Republic of the Congo (Zaire), and Australia. Russian amethysts come from the Ural
Mts., Yakutia, the Kola Peninsula. European
amethyst is known from Armenia, Germany,
the Czech Republic, Slovakia, Bulgaria,
Switzerland, Ireland. Large clear crystals
over 10 cm long are rare. One of the largest
cut amethysts is at the Natural History Museum in London (343 ct.), together with
other smaller stones (75–90 ct.). A cut amethyst weighing 1,362 ct. from Brazil is at the
Smithsonian Institution in Washington,
D.C., along with a cut stone from North
Carolina weighing 202.5 ct. Amethysts were
often set into crown jewels (the scepter of
Catherine the Great, the scepter of the British imperial crown jewels). The pope's amethyst ring is located in the Vatican treasury.

Processing: faceted cuts, cabochons, engravings, carvings
Similar minerals: spinel, fluorite, rubellite
Imitations: synthetic corundum, synthetic
amethyst, glass
Identification: specific gravity, optical
methods
Care: Protect amethyst from light, which
can cause stones to fade, especially
dark–colored stones.

*Amethyst crystals and cut stone; druse is 103 mm
wide, Murzinka, Ural Mts., Russia*

*Cut amethysts of various colors; large stone, 190 ct.,
is from Brazil.*

Chatoyant quartz varieties

History: Chatoyant quartzes have been known by that name since 1876 because of their typical color and luster. They served as talismans for farmers. Tiger's–eye was highly valued in the 19th century and was even combined with diamonds in some jewelry. Its price dropped dramatically, however, after the discovery of huge South African deposits.

Astrology: birthstone for Scorpio
Chakra: navel
Healing effects: strengthens eyesight; relieves asthma; discharge stone in water, then recharge briefly in sunlight
Host rocks: metamorphic rocks
Occurrences: The world's most famous occurrences of tiger's–eye and falcon's–eye have been mined in South Africa, near Griquatown, along the Orange River in the Door Massif. This material occurs as layers, several centimeters thick, in a massive, banded rock (jasper slate). Subsequently, tiger's–eye was found in many other places. Found in California with tremolite inclusions in 1966, tiger's–eye has also been known from Mexico and Australia, although it is usually referred to as **tiger's iron** there because of its hematite

Color: golden yellow, golden brown (*tiger's–eye*, *tiger's ore*), blue–green, blue–gray (*falcon's–eye*), red–brown (*bull's–eye*), white, gray, greenish (*cat's–eye*) • **Diaphaneity:** translucent, opaque • **Luster:** silky • **Fracture:** splintery • **Cleavage:** none • **Hardness:** 6–7 • **Streak:** white • **Specific gravity:** 2.65–2.71 • **Refractive index:** N_e–1.553, N_o–1.544 • **Birefringence:** 0.009 • **Dispersion:** 0.013 • **Pleochroism:** none • **Luminescence:** none • **Chemistry:** color caused by inclusions of other minerals (crocidolite, riebeckite, crossite, tremolite, goethite, rutile) • **Special features:** chatoyancy • **Treatment:** heating, changes color (tiger's-eye changes to bull's-eye)

or goethite content. Newer finds wer made in China, India, and Burma. Fa con's–eye (with unaltered parts of rie beckite or crossite) comes from Mexic Sri Lanka, and Australia. Russia an Ukraine have also produced tiger's iro (Kryvyy Rih region). The inclusions in th material consist of Mg–riebeckite an crossite. Its color reflects the oxidatio stage of the iron. Another occurrence c falcon's–eye is known from Austri Cat's–eye is similar to tiger's–eye, but in clusions consist of either fine amphibol or serpentine asbestos, which give stones a nice cat's–eye effect after polish

Cut falcon's–eye, South Africa.

Cut tiger's–eye, South Africa

ng. Cat's–eye occurs in Sri Lanka, India, he United States, Mexico, Brazil, and Germany (Fichtelgebirge).

Processing: cabochons, engravings, carvings

Similar minerals: chrysoberyl cat's–eye, jade

Imitations: glass

Identification: specific gravity, optical methods

Care: There are no cleaning problems unless stone contains inclusions.

Products made of tiger's–eye (yellow), bull's–eye (red), and falcon's–eye (gray), South Africa.

Tiger's iron, South Africa.

Quartz
with inclusions

History: (See **Rock crystal.**) A universally used healing gemstone, **aventurine** was very popular in ancient China, where it was named the "Emperor's stone" (Yu). As a talisman, it brought happiness, coziness, freshness, and a sound mind.

Astrology: birthstone for Cancer

Chakra: heart, secondary center in feet

Healing effects: sharpens mental acuity; discharge stone in water, then recharge briefly in the sun

Host rocks: metamorphic rocks, hydrothermal deposits, placers

Occurrences: Inclusions often give quartz a very unusual aesthetic appearance. Fine–grained quartz with very dense inclusions of fine scales of fuchsite and hematite is called aventurine (because of its typical glittery luster). Such material oc-

The quartz matrix has the same composition as rock crystal, citrine, amethyst, or smoky quartz. The overall color changes with different kinds of inclusions. Solid or fluid, the inclusions sometimes follow the growth faces of the crystals ("phantoms").

curs in India, Russia, Brazil, and Tibet. Rarer finds have been made in Austria, Germany, Spain, and Finland. Green aventurines are known from Tanzania and red–brown ones from Kenya, while white and black–and–white material comes from Russia (Siberia). Quartz with rutile inclusions of sagenite called **Venus hair** is very common in Brazil (Diamantina and

Cut quartz stones with different inclusions. (Left to right) goethite, Mangyshlak, Russia; tourmaline, Ratnapura, Sri Lanka; manganese dendrites, Brazil; cosalite, Kara–Oba, Kazakhstan; chlorite phantom, Madagascar; chlorites, Madagascar. Largest stone weighs 25 ct.

Slice of quartz crystal with goethite, 22 mm wide, Mangyshlak, Russia.

bitiara in Bahía). Rock crystal with the same type of rutile inclusions has also been found in the Alps (Switzerland, Austria, Italy), and very similar material comes from Australia (Tingha in New South Wales), Madagascar, Russia (Polar Urals), and elsewhere. Quartz with goethite inclu-

sions in some crystals was described from Morocco, the United States (New Mexico, Idaho), Germany, and the Czech Republic. Quartz with rare inclusions of pyrolusite is known from Mexico; with dumortierite inclusions, from Arizona; and with huebnerite inclusions, from Peru and the United States (Washington). Very popular is Brazilian quartz with pyrite inclusions. Helvite and cosalite inclusions are known from Kazakhstan, while hematite and gold inclusions come from California. Fine chlorite inclusions oriented along the growth faces of crystals, creating beautiful phantoms, are described from Brazil and Russia.

Processing: faceted cuts, cabochons, engravings, carvings

Similar minerals: different inclusions are also known in other transparent minerals

Imitations: glass, synthetic quartz

Identification: hardness, optical methods, specific gravity

Care: Do not use ultrasonic or steam cleaning on stones having fluid inclusions.

*Rutile needles in quartz (**sagenite**), 60 mm wide, Brazil.*

Axinite

Ca$_2$(Fe,Mn,Mg)Al$_2$
BSi$_4$O$_{15}$(OH)

From Greek *axine*
– "ax" for crystal shape

History: Although described in 1797, axinite is very rarely used as a gemstone.

Host rocks: skarns, alpine–type clefts in igneous rocks, metamorphic rocks

Occurrences: Gem–quality axinites are known from Brazil (crystals up to 20 cm in Bahía) and the United States (California, New Jersey). Axinites with an alexandrite effect occur in Nevada and also in Tanzania. Large crystals up to 20 cm are known from Mexico. Purple axinites come from Australia (Tasmania), Russia (Polar Urals), Tajikistan (Pamir Mts.), France, Switzerland, Norway, and Finland. Cut axinites over 20 ct. are rare.

Processing: faceted cuts, cabochons

Color: brown, orange–yellow (*tinzenite*), gray, purple, green, blue (*magnesioaxinite*) • **Diaphaneity:** transparent, translucent • **Luster:** glassy • **Fracture:** uneven, conchoidal • **Cleavage:** good • **Hardness:** 6.5–7, brittle • **Streak:** white • **Specific gravity:** 3.18–3.36 • **Refractive index:** N$_p$–1.693, N$_m$–1.701, N$_g$–1.704 • **Birefringence:** 0.010–0.012 • **Dispersion:** high • **Pleochroism:** strong, trichroic, visible to naked eye • **Luminescence:** sometimes purple to orange • **Chemistry:** color caused by Fe, Mn, Mg • **Special features:** rare alexandrite effect • **Treatment:** not known

Similar minerals: titanite, smoky quartz
Imitations: not known
Identification: hardness, specific gravity, optical methods
Care: Protect axinite from heat, sudden shocks, and sudden temperature changes. Clean in soap and water only; do not use ultrasonic or steam cleaning.

Typical axinite crystal, 75 mm, Puiva, Polar Urals, Russia

Epidote

$Ca_2(Fe^{3+},Al)_3$
$(SiO_4)_3(OH)$

From Greek *epididonai* - "to give besides" because crystals in some specimens had enlarged side

Color:	dark	green,	blue–green,

Color: dark green, blue–green, black–green, yellow–green, red (***piemontite***) • **Diaphaneity:** transparent to translucent • **Luster:** glassy, pearly on cleavage planes, dull • **Fracture:** conchoidal, uneven • **Cleavage:** perfect • **Hardness:** 6–7, brittle • **Streak:** gray • **Specific gravity:** 3.38–3.49 • **Refractive index:** N_p–1.715–1.751, N_m–1.725 –1.784, N_g–1.734–1.797 • **Birefringence:** 0.015–0.049 • **Dispersion:** 0.036 • **Pleochroism:** strong, visible to naked eye • **Luminescence:** none • **Chemistry:** color caused by trace amounts of Cr (***tawmawite***), Fe, Mn (piemontite) • **Special features:** none • **Treatment:** not known

Cut and polished slice of unakite, epidote–bearing decorative rock, Utah.

History: Although formally described in 1801, epidote is rarely used as a gemstone.

Host rocks: metamorphic rocks, alpine–type clefts in igneous rocks, hydrothermal deposits

Occurrences: Gemmy epidotes occur in Mexico, the United States (crystals over 15 cm from Nevada, Alaska, California, Colorado), Brazil, Australia, and New Zealand. Stones of especially high quality come from Burma (Tawmaw region); golden brown stones from Sri Lanka; and red–brown stones from Afghanistan. Epidote is also known from Pakistan, Mozambique, Kenya, Zimbabwe, and Russia (Polar Urals – crystals up to 20 cm). The world's classic epidote locality is Knappenwand in Untersulzbachtal, Austria, with crystals reaching over 20 cm in size. Nice, dark green epidotes come from the Czech Republic, Norway, and Finland. Other localities are in France and Switzerland. Epidote–bearing rock, called **unakite** and used as a decorative stone, comes from Greenland and Utah. Faceted transparent cut stones of over 5 ct. are quite rare; larger pieces are too dark and lose their transparency.

Processing: faceted cuts, cabochons

Similar minerals: verdelite, vesuvianite, actinolite

Identification: hardness, specific gravity, optical methods

Care: Protect epidote from sudden shocks and sudden temperature changes. Clean in soap and water only; do not use ultrasonic or steam cleaning.

Druse of epidote crystals, 60 mm wide, Knappenwand, Austria.

Spodumene

$LiAlSi_2O_6$

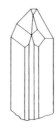

From Greek *spodoumenos*
– "burnt to ashes"
for gray variety

History: A relatively inexpensive gemstone, kunzite was formally described in 1903.
Astrology: birthstone for Taurus
Chakra: heart
Healing effects: promotes harmony of senses; banishes negative emotions; discharge stone in lukewarm water, then recharge briefly in sunlight
Host rocks: pegmatites, placers

Color: yellow–white, yellow, yellow–green, green (*hiddenite*), purple, pink (*kunzite*), gray, colorless; rarely blue, multicolored • **Diaphaneity:** transparent to translucent • **Luster:** glassy • **Fracture:** conchoidal • **Cleavage:** perfect • **Hardness:** 6.5–7.5, brittle • **Streak:** white • **Specific gravity:** 3.0–3.2 • **Refractive index:** N_p–1.653–1.670, N_m–1.660–1.669, N_g–1.665–1.682 • **Birefringence:** 0.014–0.027 • **Dispersion:** 0.017 • **Pleochroism:** visible, depending on color intensity • **Luminescence:** yellow, creamy, orange • **Chemistry:** color caused by trace amounts of Mn^{2+}, Fe^{3+}, Cr^{3+} • **Special features:** occasional chatoyancy • **Treatment:** irradiation

Hiddenite crystal, 35 mm long, Adams Mine, Hiddenite, North Carolina.

Occurrences: Spodumene, formerly called *triphane*, is a very common mineral in pegmatites, with crystals up to 13 m and weighing up to 65 t (72 short tons), although not of gem quality. It occurs in Brazil (Minas Gerais), the United States (California), Russia, and Afghanistan (Nuristan region) Chatoyant spodumene is known from Newry, Maine. Hiddenite has been found in North Carolina (Stony Point region), where it has been mined since 1879. Green spodumene comes from South Dakota (Black Hills) and California (Riverside Co.) as well as from Brazil (Minas Gerais), Madagascar, Burma, Afghanistan (Nuristan region), and Russia. Cut hiddenites are usually small, up to 2 ct., but the Natural History Museum in Vienna has a spodumene crystal measuring 3 x 0.6 cm. Kunzite often occurs in the Nuristan region of Afghanistan, in crystals up to 45 cm and weighing up to 10 kg, and in the United States (California, Massachusetts, Connecticut Maine). The largest crystal from the Pala district in California weighed 2 kg. Kunzite crystals up to 7.4 kg occur in Minas Gerais Brazil. Other localities are in Madagascar Burma, China, Russia, and recently Finland (crystals up to 7 cm). Chatoyant kunzites are known from Sri Lanka. Rough and fac-

Kunzite crystal on quartz, 66 mm, Nuristan, Afghanistan.

eted kunzites are preserved in many museum collections. The Smithsonian Institution in Washington, D.C., has cut kunzites from Brazil weighing 880, 663, and 297 ct. and one from California weighing 177 ct. A cut kunzite weighing 720 ct. is in a private collection. The Royal Ontario Museum in Toronto has a yellow–brown cut spodumene weighing 1,800 ct., while the Harvard University collection has a kunzite crystal from the Pala district weighing 2,200 g.

Processing: faceted cuts, cabochons, carvings

Similar minerals: chrysoberyl, euclase, amethyst, olivine, scapolite – for spodumene; chrysoberyl, euclase, emerald – for hiddenite; amethyst, topaz, morganite – for kunzite

Imitations: synthetic spodumene, synthetic hiddenite, colored glass

Identification: hardness, specific gravity, optical methods

Care: Spodumene is fragile and light–sensitive, esp. irradiated stones. Protect from sudden shocks and sudden temperature changes. Clean in soap and water only; do not use ultrasonic or steam cleaning.

Cut kunzite, 31.46 ct.

Cut hiddenites, 14.1 and 3.24 ct.

Staurolite

$(Fe^{2+},Mg)_2Al_9(Si,Al)_4O_{20}(O,OH)_4$
From Greek *stauros*
– "cross" for crystal shape

History: Rectangular interpenetration twins of this common mineral were used in the Middle Ages as talismans for the protection of pilgrims.

Host rocks: metamorphic rocks, placers

Occurrences: Fine crystals are known from Germany (Aschaffenburg), Switzerland (Monte Campione), Italy (Val Passaria), Austria (St. Radegrund), and also from the Czech Republic (Petrov and Desná). Large crystals come from Namibia (Gorob Mine), Madagascar, and Zambia (near Lusaka – dark blue lusakites). Staurolite also occurs in India, Greenland, Brazil, and the United States (Tennessee). The best stones have recently come from Russia (Kola Peninsula). Faceted cuts are rare and do not exceed more than a few carats.

Color: dark brown, red–brown, brown–black; rarely dark blue (*lusakite*) • **Diaphaneity:** translucent, opaque • **Luster:** glassy, silky • **Fracture:** conchoidal • **Cleavage:** good • **Hardness:** 7–7.5 • **Streak:** gray–white • **Specific gravity:** 3.65–3.83 • **Refractive index:** N_p–1.739–1.747, N_m–1.744–1.754, N_g–1.750–1.762 • **Birefringence:** 0.011–0.015 • **Dispersion:** 0.023 • **Pleochroism:** distinct – yellow–brown to brown–red • **Luminescence:** none • **Chemistry:** trace amounts of Ti, Co, Sn • **Special features:** crosslike interpenetration twins • **Treatment:** not known

Processing: cabochons, faceted cuts
Similar minerals: dravite, hessonite
Identification: hardness, specific gravity, optical methods
Care: Protect staurolite from sudden shocks and sudden temperature changes. Clean faceted stones in soap and water only; do not use ultrasonic or steam cleaning.

Staurolite crosses, 50 mm wide, Kola Peninsula, Russia

Kyanite

Al$_2$SiO$_5$
from Greek *kyanos* – "dark blue enamel, lapis lazuli"

Color: white, blue, gray, green–blue • **Diaphaneity:** transparent to translucent • **Luster:** glassy, pearly on cleavage planes • **Fracture:** uneven • **Cleavage:** perfect, good • **Hardness:** 4–7.5 (varies with direction) • **Streak:** white • **Specific gravity:** 3.55–3.66 • **Refractive index:** N$_p$–1.710–1.718, N$_m$–1.721–1.723, N$_g$–1.727–1.734 • **Birefringence:** 0.015–0.017 • **Dispersion:** 0.020 • **Pleochroism:** distinct – colorless, purple to cobalt blue • **Luminescence:** sometimes weak red • **Chemistry:** color caused by trace amounts of Fe^{2+}, Cr^{3+} and Ti^{3+} (green and blue), Fe^{3+} (green) • **Special features:** rare chatoyancy • **Treatment:** not known

History: Gemmy kyanite has only recently appeared on the market.

Host rocks: pegmatites, metamorphic rocks, placers

Occurrences: Gemmy kyanites occur in India (Punjab, Kashmir), in the gem–bearing gravels of Burma, and in Korea (near Saikori). In the United States, kyanite comes from California, Tennessee, Georgia, New Hampshire, and North Carolina (green kyanites). Nice crystals were found in Greenland; large crystals, up to 30 cm, were recently found in Australia (Harts Range region) and Brazil. African kyanites were found in Kenya, Tanzania (emerald green crystals from the Umba River region), and Namibia (green–blue crystals). Other known localities are in Switzerland, Austria, and France.

Processing: faceted cuts, cabochons
Similar minerals: aquamarine, benitoite, sapphire
Identification: hardness, optical methods
Care: Protect from shocks and temperature changes. Clean in soap and water only.

Kyanite, 40 mm wide, India.

Danburite

$CaB_2(SiO_4)_2$

After Danbury, Connecticut

History: Danburite was discovered in Danbury, Connecticut, in 1839.

Host rocks: pegmatites, metamorphic, and sedimentary rocks

Occurrences: A common mineral, danburite is rare as a gemstone. Honey yellow crystals (Baja California) and colorless to pinkish crystals up to 10 cm (Charcas) are known from Mexico. Danburite also occurs in Bolivia, Burma (large white and yellow crystals), Japan (colorless crystals up to 9 cm), Russia (Dalnegorsk – colorless and green crystals up to 20 cm), and Madagascar (large yellow–brown crystals). Large cut stones can exceed 200 ct.

Processing: faceted cuts, cabochons

Similar minerals: citrine, apatite, topaz

Color: colorless, wine yellow, gray, brown, pink • **Diaphaneity:** transparent to translucent • **Luster:** glassy, greasy • **Fracture:** conchoidal, uneven • **Cleavage:** indistinct • **Hardness:** 7–7.5 • **Streak:** white • **Specific gravity:** 2.97–3.03 • **Refractive index:** N_p–1.630, N_m–1.633, N_g–1.647 • **Birefringence:** 0.006–0.008 • **Dispersion:** 0.017 • **Pleochroism:** weak – yellowish in colored stones • **Luminescence:** sometimes blue, green–blue, white • **Chemistry:** may contain trace amounts of REE • **Special features:** none • **Treatment:** irradiation

Imitations: none

Identification: hardness, specific gravity optical methods

Care: Clean in soap and water only; do not use ultrasonic or steam cleaning.

Danburite, originally colorless, turns brown after irradiation. Irradiated cut stone, 6 ct., Dalnegorsk, Russia

Benitoite

BaTiSi$_3$O$_9$

After San Benito Co., California

Color: blue, blue–gray, colorless • **Diaphaneity:** transparent to translucent • **Luster:** glassy • **Fracture:** conchoidal, uneven • **Cleavage:** indistinct • **Hardness:** 6–7 • **Streak:** white • **Specific gravity:** 3.64–3.68 • **Refractive index:** N$_e$–1.800–1.804, N$_o$–1,756–1.757 • **Birefringence:** 0.047 • **Dispersion:** 0.044 • **Pleochroism:** strongly dichroic • **Luminescence:** intense blue • **Chemistry:** soluble in HF • **Special features:** none • **Treatment:** some heated stones turn orange

History: Benitoite was discovered in San Benito Co., California, in 1907.

Host rocks: igneous rocks

Occurrences: The type locality (San Benito Co., California) is basically the only producer of gemmy benitoite, which occurs in serpentinite dikes associated with neptunite and natrolite. Crystals are quite rare, usually reaching about 1 cm, although crystals up to 4 cm have been found. A cut benitoite weighing 7.80 ct. is at the Smithsonian Institution in Washington, D.C.

Benitoite, 20 mm high, Dallas Gem Mine, San Benito Co., California.

Processing: faceted cuts

Similar minerals: sapphire, cordierite (iolite), indicolite

Imitations: none

Identification: hardness, specific gravity, optical methods

Care: Protect benitoite from sudden temperature changes and HF. Clean in soap and water only; do not use ultrasonic or steam cleaning.

Tanzanite
(zoisite variety)

$Ca_2Al_3(SiO_4)_3(OH)$

After Tanzania

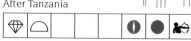

History: Known in Tanzania since long ago, and today one of the most popular gemstones, tanzanite was first described in 1967 by the Indian prospector Manuel de Souza, who originally thought he had discovered a sapphire deposit. It was later described as a zoisite variety by the German Gemological Society. Tanzanite became famous due to a necklace with five faceted tanzanites of extraordinary quality owned by Elizabeth Taylor.

Astrology: birthstone for Sagittarius
Chakra: throat
Healing effects: strengthens heart; used to treat mental illnesses; discharge stone in lukewarm water, then recharge briefly in sunlight
Host rocks: metamorphic rocks, pegmatites

Color: blue, green–blue, blue–purple, brown; rarely yellow, colorless • **Diaphaneity:** transparent • **Luster:** glassy, pearly on cleavage planes, silky • **Fracture:** conchoidal, uneven • **Cleavage:** perfect • **Hardness:** 6–6.5, brittle • **Streak:** white • **Specific gravity:** 3.35 • **Refractive index:** N_p–1.692, N_m–1.693, N_g–1.700 • **Birefringence:** 0.009 • **Dispersion:** 0.019 • **Pleochroism:** very strong – blue, purple, green – trichroic, visible to naked eye • **Luminescence:** none • **Chemistry:** color caused by trace amounts of V^{3+}, Cr^{3+}; can intensify at 700°C • **Special features:** alexandrite effect, occasional chatoyancy • **Treatment:** heating

Occurrences: Tanzanite comes from Merelani in the Gerevi Hills, near the towns of Arusha and Moshi in Tanzania. Its prismatic crystals with typical vertical striation occur in gneisses with pegmatitic–hydrothermal dikes. Very nice tanzanite rough and cut stones are preserved at the Smithsonian Institution in Washington, D.C. A cut stone weighing over 200 ct. and

Different–colored, untreated tanzanites; largest, 3 ct., Tanzania.

Cut tanzanite, 16.78 ct., Arusha, Tanzania.

*Pink zoisite (**thulite**) is basic constituent of decorative gabbro, Kola Peninsula, Russia.*

Tanzanite crystal, 46 mm long, Arusha, Tanzania.

a cat's–eye tanzanite weighing 18.2 ct. have been reported in the literature. Tanzanites are set into all kinds of jewelry, often together with diamonds. Their color can be intensified by heating to 400–500°C.

Processing: faceted cuts, cabochons

Similar minerals: sapphire, spinel, cordierite, dumortierite

Imitations: doublets, glass, synthetic corundum

Identification: hardness, specific gravity, optical methods

Care: Protect tanzanite's perfect cleavage from sudden shocks and sudden temperature changes. Clean in soap and water only; do not use ultrasonic or steam cleaning.

Olivine (peridot)

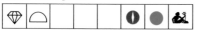

$(Mg,Fe)_2SiO_4$

From Latin *oliva* – "olive,"
hence "olive green"

Color: yellow–green, olive green, green–black, black–brown • **Diaphaneity:** transparent to translucent • **Luster:** greasy to glassy • **Fracture:** conchoidal • **Cleavage:** indistinct to poor Hardness: 6.5–7 • **Streak:** white, yellowish • **Specific gravity:** 3.27–4.20 (depending on Mg and Fe content) • **Refractive index:** N_p–1.649–1.827, N_m–1.664–1.869, N_g–1.684–1.879 • **Birefringence:** 0.033–0.040 • **Dispersion:** 0.020 • **Pleochroism:** weak – colorless to light green, green to olive green • **Luminescence:** none • **Chemistry:** olivine is group name for minerals from isomorphous series *forsterite* (Mg_2SiO_4) – *fayalite* (Fe_2SiO_4) • **Special features:** rare chatoyancy • **Treatment:** not known

History: Known already to the ancient Greeks, olivine is or has been also called fayalite, forsterite, peridot, and ***chrysolite***. It was later used in church jewelry and objects. A lovers' stone during the Baroque era, olivine was believed to protect people from heartache and misfortune.

Astrology: birthstone for Virgo, Pisces (Babylonians), Leo (Egyptians, Byzantines)

Chakra: heart

Healing effects: promotes digestion, healthy functioning of spleen; lowers fever; used to treat constipation, also melancholy; discharge stone in water, then recharge briefly in sunlight

Host rocks: ultrabasic rocks, pegmatites

Occurrences: Historically, the most important deposits of olivine were located in Egypt (Zebirget Island in Red Sea), where mining activity dates back about 3,500 years. Deposits also occur in Burma (Mogok region) and in Brazil (Minas Gerais and Permanbuco), where it has been mined together with other gemstones. Good–quality olivines occur in the United States (New Mexico, Hawaii, and especially Arizona – aggregates up to 20 cm) and in the basalts of Mexico, while light green stones come from Australia. Fine crystals have been found on Ross Island, Antarctica. Less im-

Olivine crystals; larger, 49 mm long, Pakistan.

Cut olivines (forsterite); middle stone, 65 ct., Supat, Kohistan, Pakistan.

portant occurrences are in South Africa, Tanzania, Kenya, the Democratic Republic of the Congo (Zaire), and Somalia. Olivine is associated with diamonds in the Kolyma River basin in Siberia, Russia, where it forms black fayalite crystals up to 20 cm, and occurs in the Ural and Sayany Mts. Recent olivine finds have been made in Mongolia, Afghanistan, and also in Pakistan, where very fine olivine crystals, suitable for faceting, have been discovered. Historically important olivine occurrences are located in the Czech Republic (Kozákov, Smrčí). Light green olivines are known from Norway, Greenland, Germany (Eifel region), and Italy. Clear, yellow–green cut stones may exceed 100 ct. Many large cut olivines have their own history and significance, and are among the highlights of many museum collections. The Smithsonian Institution in Washington, D.C. has a 310 ct. gem from Zebirget Island and a 287 ct. gem from Burma, while the Diamond Fund in Moscow has a cut olivine weighing 192.6 ct., also from Zebirget Island.

Processing: faceted cuts, cabochons

Similar minerals: chrysoberyl, prehnite, moldavite

Imitation: synthetic spinel, synthetic corundum

Identification: hardness, specific gravity, optical methods

Care: Olivine is fragile and should be handled carefully. Protect stones from acids. Soldering solution may damage surface. Clean in soap and water only; do not use ultrasonic or steam cleaning.

Cut olivine with typical ludwigite inclusions, 4.5 ct, Pakistan.

*Polished section of **pallasite** meteorite (olivine forms grains in iron matrix), 70 mm wide.*

Chalcedony

(quartz variety)

SiO_2

After Chalcedon, ancient
Greek city in Asia Minor

History: Used to make a wide variety of tools in prehistoric times, and only later as a gemstone, chalcedony has been dyed since the Middle Ages. It is believed to have aphrodisiac powers, attracting men to women, and to protect its owner from anger and melancholy.

Astrology: birthstone for Capricorn

Chakra: throat

Healing effects: stops bleeding; used to treat menopause problems, also diseases of throat; discharge stone in running water, then recharge briefly in sunlight

Host rocks: volcanic rocks, hydrothermal deposits, weathering zones, sedimentary rocks

Color: white, gray, gray–blue; rarely other colors • **Diaphaneity:** translucent to opaque • **Luster:** glassy, greasy, dull • **Fracture:** conchoidal, uneven • **Cleavage:** indistinct or none • **Hardness:** 6–7 • **Streak:** white • **Specific gravity:** 2.50–2.70 • **Refractive index:** N_e–1.539–1.544, N_o–1.526–1.535 • **Birefringence:** 0.004–0.009 • **Dispersion:** none • **Pleochroism:** none • **Luminescence:** sometimes weak to intense yellow–green, yellow, white, light blue • **Chemistry:** color is caused by trace amounts of Fe, Mn, Ni, Cr, different inclusions. • **Special features:** rare iridescence • **Treatment:** heating, dyeing

Chalcedony; stalactite is 15 mm long, Podmoskovye, Russia

Chalcedony objects from various localities.

Occurrences: A cryptocrystalline variety of quartz known from all over the world, chalcedony comes in many varieties according to its color, texture, and inclusions (esp. chlorites and hematite): agate, carnelian, chrysoprase, *flint*, heliotrope, jasper, *plasma*, *prase*, onyx, sardonyx. Very important finds were historically made in India, in Deccan basalt traps, weathering zones, and placers. Chalcedony commonly occurs in Saudi Arabia, Yemen, Taiwan, and Iraq. It also comes from the United States (Florida; California – blue; Oregon; Arizona – pink, purple; Colorado; Idaho), Canada, Mexico, Brazil, and Uruguay. Other localities include New Zealand, Australia, Iceland, and the Faroe Islands. Principal African occurrences are in Namibia, South Africa, Botswana, Morocco, Libya, Egypt, Ethiopia, and Madagascar. Large chalcedony deposits are located in Russia (Ural Mts., Transbaikalia, Sakhalin Island). It has also been found in Kazakhstan, Armenia, Georgia, and Azerbaijan. Chalcedony has long been known from the Czech Republic (Podkrkonoší region) and Germany. Less important occurrences are in Austria, Slovakia, Poland, Italy (Sicily, Sardinia), Bulgaria, and Romania.

Processing: cabochons, carvings, engravings
Similar minerals: smithsonite, opal
Imitations: glass
Identification: hardness, specific gravity, optical methods
Care: Protect chalcedony from HF. There are no cleaning problems unless stone contains inclusions.

Plasma, Hrubšice, Czech Republic.

Chrysoprase

(quartz variety)

SiO_2

From Greek *chrysos + prason*
= "gold leek," hence "golden green"

	◠	▢	🐎		●	🏹

Color: emerald green, blue–green, apple green • **Diaphaneity:** translucent, opaque • **Luster:** glassy, greasy, dull • **Fracture:** conchoidal, uneven • **Cleavage:** indistinct or none • **Hardness:** 6–7 • **Streak:** white • **Specific gravity:** 2.50–2.70 • **Refractive index:** N_e–1.539–1.544, N_o–1.526–1.535 • **Birefringence:** 0.004–0.005 • **Dispersion:** none • **Pleochroism:** none • **Luminescence:** none • **Chemistry:** color caused by trace amounts of Ni or Cr • **Special features:** none • **Treatment:** not known

History: The ancient Greeks and Romans made brooches, bracelets, necklaces, and rings out of chrysoprase, which was later used for decoration inside churches and cathedrals. As a talisman, it was believed to protect its owner from evil looks, curses, and envy.

Astrology: birthstone for Sagittarius, Scorpio (Egyptians)

Chakra: heart

Healing effects: calms heart; stops bleeding; discharge stone in lukewarm water, then recharge briefly in sunlight

Host rocks: weathering zones of serpentinite bodies

Occurrences: Although a rather uncommon mineral elsewhere, it is widespread in Arizona (Keystone), California, North Carolina, and Oregon. Chrysoprase also occurs in Brazil, Australia, New Caledonia, Tasmania, and many parts of India. African localities are in Tanzania, Zimbabwe, and South Africa. Many occurrences are known from Russia, and historically important chrysoprase finds were made in Poland (Szklary). Chrysoprase was recently discovered in Serbia (Golesh) and in Kazakhstan, which has produced high–quality material in masses weighing over 1 kg.

Processing: cabochons, engravings, carvings, plates, faceted cuts (rare)

Similar minerals: jade, prehnite, variscite

Imitations: artificially dyed chalcedony

Identification: hardness, specific gravity, optical methods

Care: Chrysoprase fades when exposed to heat or light. Protect stones from HF. There are no cleaning problems unless stone contains inclusions.

Chrysoprase; larges cabochon, 40 mm Szklary, Poland.

Carnelian

(quartz variety)

SiO_2

from "cornelian," altered by association with Vulgar Latin *caro* – "flesh, meat," hence "dark red, brown–red"

Color: dark red, orange–red, brown–red • **Diaphaneity:** translucent • **Luster:** glassy, greasy, dull • **Fracture:** conchoidal, uneven • **Cleavage:** indistinct or none • **Hardness:** 6–7 • **Streak:** white • **Specific gravity:** 2.50–2.70 • **Refractive index:** N_e–1.539–1.544, N_o–1.526–1.535 • **Birefringence:** 0.004–0.009 • **Dispersion:** none • **Chemistry:** color caused by trace amount of Fe • **Special features:** inclusions of hematite and other minerals • **Treatment:** not known

Similar minerals: jasper
Imitations: colored chalcedony, glass
Identification: hardness, specific gravity, optical methods
Care: Carnelian may fade in light. There are no cleaning problems unless stone contains inclusions.

Carnelian in matrix, Brdo near Nová Paka, Czech Republic.

Carnelian carving, 100 mm high, Russian work, second half of 19th century.

History: Carnelian was mined more than 5,000 years ago to produce colored sealing wax, jewelry, and decorative objects. It was believed to protect people from quarrels, toothaches, and mental diseases, to calm tempers, and to bring happiness.
Astrology: birthstone for Aries, Cancer (medieval astrologers)
Chakra: sacral
Healing effects: stops bleeding; lowers fever; stimulates sexual glands; strengthens heart; revitalizes; discharge stone in water, then recharge briefly in sunlight
Host rocks: volcanic rocks, weathering zones
Occurrences: The earliest sources of carnelian were in India, Saudi Arabia, and Egypt. Very important localities are situated in Brazil (Rio Grande do Sul) and the United States (Colorado, Utah, Nebraska). It also occurs in Australia, Russia (Far East, Chukotka, Yakutia), the Czech Republic (Podkrkonoší region), Germany, and Romania.
Processing: cabochons, table cuts, small carvings, engravings

Agate
(quartz variety)

SiO_2

After Achates
(now Dirillo) River, Sicily

History: Agate tools date back to over 8,000 years ago. Agates from India, usually gray, gray–white, and gray–blue, and associated with basalt lava flows and their weathering products on the Deccan Plateau, have been known since earliest history. Used by the Scythians and mentioned by Theophrastos, agate was the most popular stone in ancient Greece and Rome, where it was dyed, made into decorative objects, and carved into cameos (famous Gemma Augustea in Vienna). As a talisman, agate was believed to protect people from poisons and to calm storms and even hurricanes.

Astrology: birthstone for Taurus

Chakra: base

Healing effects: strengthens sexual organs; sharpens eyesight; relieves pain; used to treat epilepsy, also insomnia; discharge stone in water, then recharge briefly charge in sunlight

Host rocks: volcanic rocks (paleobasalts, basalts, rhyolites, porphyries), hydrothermal deposits, weathering zones, sedimentary rocks, placers

Occurrences: Agates are known from all over the world. Especially beautiful are

Color: always multicolored; mostly gray, gray–blue, white; often also blue–white, blue, pinkish, creamy white, reddish; rarely green–blue red–brown, brown, yellow–brown, orange, gray–black; greenish agates are also known • **Diaphaneity:** translucent, opaque • **Luster:** glassy, greasy, dull • **Fracture:** conchoidal, uneven • **Cleavage:** indistinct or none • **Hardness:** 6–7 • **Streak:** white • **Specific gravity:** 2.50–2.70 • **Refractive index:** N_e–1.539–1.544, N_o–1.526 –1.535 • **Birefringence:** 0.004–0.009 • **Dispersion:** none • **Pleochroism:** none • **Luminescence:** sometimes weak to intense yellow, greenish, light blue, white • **Chemistry:** color caused by trace amounts of Fe, Mn, Ni, Cr, other metals • **Special features:** iridescence • **Treatment:** dyeing, heating

stones with more than two alternating colors (cold and warm hues), intensified by the agate's characteristic banding (usually concentric, more rarely parallel). Some agates have more than 15,000 bands in 1 cm. Others are ball–shaped, eye–like, oolithic or dendritic (***moss agate***). Agates sometimes have a cavity in their centers, which can be filled with crystals of amethyst, smoky quartz, calcite, or zeolites. The color of agates depends on the amount of

Artificially dyed agate, 180 mm wide (original color is on both margins), Brazil.

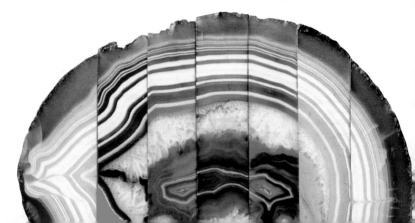

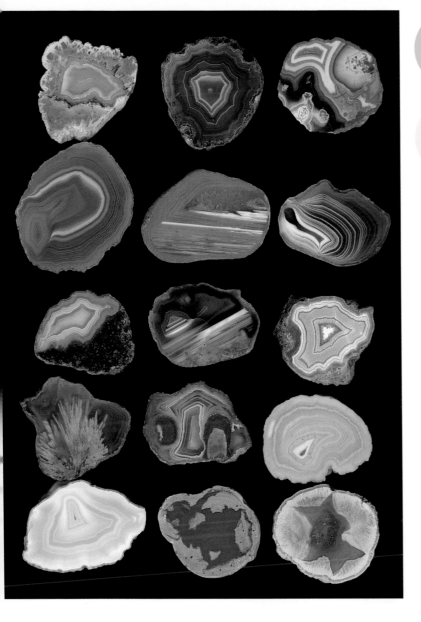

Agates from different localities, life–size unless otherwise noted.

From upper left: Slovakia, Mexico, Australia (3x), Botswana, Czech Republic, Mongolia, Czech Republic (3x), Poland, Australia (3x).

Agate, St. Egidien, Germany.

inclusions of other minerals (chlorite, hematite, limonite, goethite, celadonite), or it can be caused by trace amounts of other elements. Many varieties are distinguished on the basis of texture or iridescence: **Aztec agate**, **Brazilian agate**, **breccia agate**, **coral agate**, **dendritic agate**, **ocellar agate**, **ruin agate**, and **star agate**. Red, orange, and yellow–brown agates come from China and the Mongolian part of the Gobi Desert (Akr–Bogdo, Dalan–Turu, Ulugai–Hid). Their texture is concentric, combined, parallel, and banded, and they

Fire agate, 28 mm wide, Arizona.

often have a cavity in the center (geode) filled with amethyst, smoky quartz, or rock crystal. Beautiful agates have also been found in Yemen (Wadi – Khinai), Iraq (Rutha region), Indonesia, and Australia. In 1827, the world's largest agate deposits, over about 1.5 million km^2 (580,000 mi^2), were discovered in the basalt lava flows and weathering zones of Brazil and Uruguay. Agates from this region are known by their typical association with amethyst geodes. Their colors are rather monotonous

Agate, Horní Halže, Czech Republic.

(gray, gray–blue), but they can be very easily dyed. One of the largest stones, found in 1900, measured 10 x 2 x 1 m. Agates are also known from Nicaragua (San Juan de Limai region – white and gray agates), Mexico (multicolored and **fire agates**) and the United States (California, Oregon, Idaho, Wyoming, Montana, Iowa, and Florida). Many deposits are known from Africa, in the seashore placers of Namibia, Madagascar (Antsirabé region), Mozambique (Lebombo region), South Africa, Botswana, and Lesotho. Very fine agates are found in Ethiopia, Morocco, the Democratic Republic of the Congo (Zaire; Kasai River basin), Uganda, Angola, Egypt (Jebel Abu Diyeiba, known for 3,000 years). Important agate deposits are found in Russia, Armenia, Georgia, and Azerbaijan. Agates come also from the northern part of Russia (Timan region), the Ural Mts., Siberia, and the Amur region. Fine blue and orange–red agates have been found in

Polygonal agate, Brazil.

Chukotka and Kamchatka. Agates also occur in Kazakhstan, Uzbekistan, and Turkmenistan (Tavaku produced black agates). Many agate localities are known in Europe, some already mined in the Middle Ages. One famous area is in the vicinity of Idar–Oberstein and St. Egidien in Germany. Other occurrences are in Poland, Norway, Scotland, Greece, Bulgaria (Rodopy Mts.), Italy (Val di Fassa), Finland,

Moss agate, India.

and the Faroe Islands. Historically important deposits were mined in the Czech Republic (Podkrkonoší region), with peak activity during the reign of the Rudolf II. The most important localities there are Kozákov, Levín, Zeleznice, Rvácov, and Frýdštejn. Agates and agate objects are preserved in most of the major museums, most notably at Moscow's Kremlin Armory and Fersman Mineralogical Museum

and at St. Petersburg's Hermitage. Beautiful lapidary agate objects are also to be found at the Kunsthistorisches Museum in Vienna, the National Library in Paris, and in the old agate–cutting centers of Turnov (Czech Republic) and Idar–Oberstein (Germany).

Processing: cabochons, table cuts, cameos, carvings, engravings, tumbled stones
Similar minerals: opal, banded fluorite
Imitations: glass
Identification: specific gravity, optical methods

Agate, Mexico.

Care: Protect agate from sudden temperature changes, which may cause color to change, and from HF. There are no cleaning problems unless stone contains inclusions.

Agate–onyx, Brazil.

Jasper

(quartz variety)

SiO₂

From Greek *iaspis* – "jasper"

History: Jasper, which often contains inclusions of opal or quartz, has long been used as a gemstone. It has served as raw material for making all kinds of sealing sticks, carvings, objects, and engravings. Old legends call jasper the mother of all the stones. It was believed to protect its owner from vertigo, ghosts, and vanity in affairs of the heart.

Astrology: birthstone for Pisces, Virgo (Babylonians), Aquarius (Egyptians)

Chakra: base

Healing effects: whets appetite; promotes healthy functioning of stomach, intestines, liver; limits bleeding, formation of hemorrhoids; used to treat women's ailments, also gout, urinary problems; discharge stone in water, then recharge briefly in sunlight

Host rocks: low–temperature veins, metamorphic and sedimentary rocks, weathering zones, placers

Occurrences: Historical finds were made on the Deccan Plateau in India and are associated with agates. Jasper has also been found in China and Mongolia. Many

Color: most often different hues of red, purple–red, yellow, green, white, brown; color caused by inclusions of other minerals; green jasper with a regular pattern of red dots is called *heliotrope* or *bloodstone* • **Diaphaneity:** opaque • **Luster:** dull • **Fracture:** conchoidal, uneven • **Cleavage:** indistinct or none • **Hardness:** 6–7 • **Streak:** different, depending on inclusions • **Specific gravity:** 2.58–2.91 • **Refractive index:** like chalcedony • **Birefringence:** none • **Dispersion:** none • **Pleochroism:** none • **Luminescence:** none • **Chemistry:** trace amounts of Fe, Mn • **Special features:** none • **Treatment:** dyeing, heating

occurrences are known from the United States. Black jasper–bearing rocks are known from North Carolina; yellow, red and white jasper from Kansas; banded jasper from Texas, Arizona, California, Vermont, Wyoming, Idaho. Red and greenish jasper was also produced in South Africa and Egypt (Nile River basin). Other deposits are found in Uganda and Libya. Large and famous jasper deposits in Russia have been mined intensively since the Middle Ages. The Ural Mts. are especially known for their jasper. Big boulders weighing several tons have been found in the middle and southern parts of the Ural Mts., and jasper has been mined near the town of Orsk. Other occurrences are known from Georgia, Poland, Finland, Germany, Italy

Jasper, Oregon.

Jasper, Oregon.

Jasper, India.

Jasper–heliotrope, India.

nd France. Czech deposits have also been nown since the Middle Ages (Podkrko-oší region). Many churches and cathedrals were decorated with polished jasper labs, especially during the reign of Charles IV in the 14th century (St. Cross chapel

in Karlštejn castle, decorated with 2,496 stones).

Processing: cabochons, table cuts, carvings

Similar minerals: other quartz varieties

Imitations: glass

Identification: optical methods

Care: Protect jasper from sudden temperature changes, which may cause color to change. There are no cleaning problems unless stone contains inclusions.

Multicolored jaspers from various localities.

Jasper, India.

Jasper, Germany.

Other quartz family gemstones

Different kinds of *iron quartz*, flints, as well as silicified plants and animals belong to this broad, poorly defined group.

History: Different quartz family materials, now known by various local names, first appeared as a raw material for making lapidary objects in prehistoric times. They have been a favorite material for distinctive sculptures, carvings, facing, and jewelry.

Astrology: birthstone for Pisces

Chakras: base (red varieties), sacral (orange varieties)

Healing effects: restores vitality, mental balance; discharge stone in water, then recharge briefly in sunlight

Host rocks: metamorphic rocks, hydrothermal deposits, sedimentary rocks, placers

Occurrences: Iron quartz, used for mosaics, facing, and some exceptionally large pieces, occurs in many countries, most importantly Brazil, India, Ukraine, Kazakhstan, and Russia, where various decorative objects have been made from it. Very fine iron quartz comes from the Czech Republic (Hořovice, vicinity of Prague). Different varieties of flints have been known from Poland, Germany, Libya,

Color: red, orange, yellow, brown, gray, beige, black; mostly multicolored • **Diaphaneity:** opaque • **Luster:** glassy, dull, greasy • **Fracture:** conchoidal, uneven • **Cleavage:** indistinct or none • **Hardness:** variable, depending on different inclusions, up to 7 • **Streak:** white; sometimes other colors, depending on inclusions • **Specific gravity:** 2.56–3.00 (depending on inclusions) • **Refractive index:** N_e–1.553, N_o–1.544 • **Birefringence:** 0.009 • **Dispersion:** 0.013 • **Pleochroism:** none • **Luminescence:** none • **Chemistry:** color caused by trace amounts of Fe, other elements, inclusions of other minerals • **Special features:** significant color and structural variability • **Treatment:** some are heated or exposed to the sun to enhance color

Australia, and Cuba. Locally abundant i the Czech Republic (Podkrkonoší regior vicinity of Plzen, southern Moravia), *petri fied wood* has been found in India, Iraq Syria, Mongolia, the United States Greece, Nicaragua, Argentina, and Austra lia. Silicified "*dinosaur bones*" come fron the United States and are quite popula among collectors. Other quartz family ma terials occur in Germany, Morocco, Alge ria, Iraq, Libya, Egypt, Yemen, India, and Vietnam.

Processing: different small lapidary ob

Iron quartz, Řevnice, Czech Republic.

Iron quartz, Hořovice, Czech Republic.

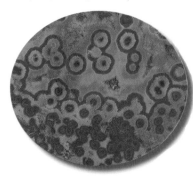

Chert, *Vrančice u Milína, Czech Republic.*

Chert, *Krzemiónki, Poland.*

ects, mosaics, cabochons
Similar minerals: jasper, agate
Imitations: not known

Identification: optical methods, hardness
Care: There are no cleaning problems unless stone contains inclusions.

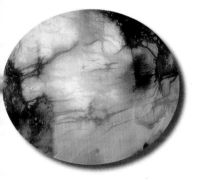

Petrified wood, *Arizona.*

Petrified wood (psaronia), *Czech Republic.*

Turritella agate, *United States.*

Petrified "dinosaur bone," *United States.*

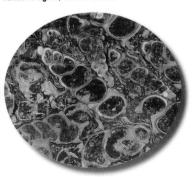

Jadeite

$Na(Al,Fe^{3+})Si_2O_6$

From (obsolete) Spanish
(*piedra de*) *ijada* – "loin stone"

History: Tools made from jadeite date back to Neolithic times. Known to the Mayans and Aztecs, it was the symbol of state power in ancient China, where it was worth more than gold, called the "Emperor's stone" (Yu), and used for making religious objects. Jadeite was believed to protect its owner from discomfort and misfortune.

Astrology: birthstone for Cancer
Chakra: heart
Healing effects: energizes; lifts spirits; relieves headaches, insomnia; used to treat urinary ailments; discharge stone in water, then recharge for some time in sunlight

Color: green–white, green, light green (*albite–jadeite*), emerald green (*imperial jade*), gray; rarely reddish, brown, purple, green–black (*chloromelanite*), red–orange • **Diaphaneity:** translucent, opaque • **Luster:** glassy • **Fracture:** splintery • **Cleavage:** none • **Hardness:** 6.5–7 • **Streak:** white • **Specific gravity:** 3.25–3.36 • **Refractive index:** N_p–1.640–1.658, N_m–1.645–1.663, N_g–1.652–1.673 • **Birefringence:** 0.012–0.020 • **Dispersion:** none • **Pleochroism:** none • **Luminescence:** sometimes weak white • **Chemistry:** color caused by trace amounts of Fe^{2+}, Fe^{3+}, sometimes Cr^{3+} (imperial jade) • **Special features:** rare chatoyancy • **Treatment:** heating, dyeing

Host rocks: metamorphic rocks
Occurrences: The most important deposits of jadeite were located in the Uru River

*Jadeite carving,
50 mm high, Burma.*

...deite sculpture, ...0 mm, contemporary Chinese work.

...lley (Tawmaw, Mainmaw, Pangvaw) in ...orthern Burma. Other localities, in the My-...kyina Province, produced the best raw material (imperial jade). Chinese jadeite occurs mainly in Yunnan Province and Tibet. ...ocalities in the Western Hemisphere in-...lude the United States (California), where ...block weighing 160 t (176 short tons) was ...ound, Guatemala, Mexico, and Colombia. ...urther deposits are in southern Australia, ...apua – New Guinea and New Zealand. ...ess important localities are in Kazakhstan ...ear the Balkhash Lake) and in Russia (Ural ...ts., Sayany Mts.). Small amounts of jade-...e were produced from Armenia, Greenland ...iros Island), and Italy. Chloromelanites ...ave been found in Burma, Italy, France,

and Switzerland. Jadeite lapidary objects are in the collections of many museums, including the Hermitage in St. Petersburg, the Museum of Eastern Cultures in Moscow, and the American Museum of Natural History in New York.

Processing: cabochons, carving, sculptures

Similar minerals: nephrite, amazonite, aventurine, prehnite, hydrogrossular, serpentine, agalmatolite

Imitations: hydrogrossular, serpentine, glass

Identification: hardness, specific gravity, optical methods

Care: Jadeite may be damaged by flame. There are no cleaning problems unless stone contains inclusions.

Nephrite
(actinolite variety)

$Ca_2(Mg,Fe^{2+})_5Si_8O_{22}(OH)_2$

From Greek
nephros – "kidney"

History: Because of its toughness, nephrite was first used to make tools and only later to make decorative lapidary objects. Known since prehistoric times, it was highly prized in Babylonia, in Meso-america, and in ancient China, where it was used in many religious ceremonies. The Sumerians believed nephrite had the power to solve life's unexpected problems.

Astrology: birthstone for Cancer
Chakra: heart
Healing effects: used to treat kidney and other urinary ailments, also psychological disturbances; discharge stone in water, then recharge briefly in sunlight
Host rocks: metamorphic rocks, placers
Occurrences: More common than jadeite, nephrite sometimes occurs in enormous blocks. Russia has produced blocks weighing 4–5 t (4.5–5.5 short tons; Sayany Mts.), and a block weighing 30 t (33 short tons) was reported from Burma. Historically, important deposits are located in

Color: green, gray–green, emerald green, dark green; rarely white, bluish, brownish, yellow, spinach green ("*Russian jade*"), black • **Diaphaneity:** translucent, opaque • **Luster:** glassy, greasy, silky • **Fracture:** splintery • **Cleavage:** none • **Hardness:** 6–6.5, brittle but very tough • **Streak:** white • **Specific gravity:** 2.90–3.02 • **Refractive index:** N_p–1.599–1.618, N_m–1.613–1.633, N_g–1.625–1.641 • **Birefringence:** 0.027 (theoretical; practically none) • **Dispersion:** none • **Pleochroism:** distinct (often masked by its fibrous texture) – yellow, brown to green • **Luminescence:** none • **Chemistry:** color caused by trace amounts of Cr, Ni, Mn • **Special features:** chatoyancy • **Treatment:** dyeing

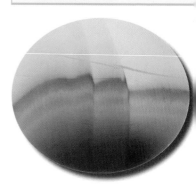

Nephrite polished section, Mexico.

Nephrite, Jordanów, Poland.

China (Xinjiang Autonomous Region, Kunlun Mts., and near Kashi). Important occurrences are also in New Zealand where the native Maoris mined it before the Europeans arrived. This material, from the Arakuara River and Wakapitu Lake, is translucent and considered to be the most beautiful in the world. Nephrite is known from Australia and New Caledonia, as well as from the United States (California, Oregon, Utah, Wyoming), Canada, Brazil, Mexico, and Zimbabwe. Chatoyant neph-

Nephrite bowl, 160 mm wide, Russian work, second half of 19th century.

...rite has been found in Taiwan and in Alaska. Russian nephrite has been found in the Sayany Mts., the Ural Mts., Yakutia, and Tuva. Smaller deposits are known from Kazakhstan, Poland (Jordanów), and Jordan. Nephrite objects are in many treasuries all over the world. The nephrite gravestone of Timur (Tamerlane) is located in the Gur–Emir mausoleum in Samarkand, Uzbekistan.

Processing: cabochons, table cuts, carvings, lapidary objects

Similar minerals: hydrogrossular, amazonite, prehnite, serpentine, agalmatolite, jadeite

Imitations: hydrogrossular, vesuvianite (Californian jade), bowenite, Korean jade (serpentine)

Identification: hardness, specific gravity, optical methods

Care: Nephrite may be damaged by flame. There are no cleaning problems unless stone contains inclusions.

Nephrite polished section, New Zealand.

Potassium feldspars

KAlSi$_3$O$_8$

Originally, "potash feldspars" because they enriched soil upon weathering; from German *Feldspath* – "field spar"

Color: colorless (*adularia*), yellow, reddish (*sunstone*), green (*amazonite*), bluish (*moonstone*) • **Diaphaneity:** transparent to translucent, opaque • **Luster:** glassy, pearly • **Fracture:** conchoidal • **Cleavage:** good • **Hardness:** 6–6.5 • **Streak:** white • **Specific gravity:** 2.54–2.63 • **Refractive index:** N$_p$, N$_m$, N$_g$: **orthoclase** 1.520–1.528, 1.524–1.533, 1.525–1.537; **microcline** 1.514–1.529, 1.518–1.533, 1.521–1.539; **sanidine** 1.518–1.527, 1.522–1.534, 1.522–1.534 • **Birefringence:** 0.004–0.010 • **Dispersion:** 0.012 (orthoclase) • **Pleochroism:** weak or none • **Luminescence:** weak yellow, white, green, bluish • **Chemistry:** color caused by trace amounts of Fe^{2+} • **Special features:** chatoyancy, asterism, iridescence (sunstone, moonstone) • **Treatment:** irradiation, wax proofing

History: Potassium feldspars are very important rock–forming minerals. Recognized as a gemstone since the Egyptian pharaohs (amulets from the 14th century B.C.), amazonite was prized in the Middle East. Decorative potassium feldspars have only recently become popular among collectors. Adularia (orthoclase variety) is said to protect the subconscious by helping to refine and balance the emotions.

Astrology: birthstone for Libra

Chakras: heart (amazonite), throat (moonstone)

Healing effects: strengthens heart (amazonite); used to treat women's ailments, also diseases of throat (moonstone); discharge stone in lukewarm water, then recharge briefly in sunlight

Host rocks: igneous and metamorphic rocks, pegmatites, hydrothermal deposits, placers

Occurrences: Chatoyant orthoclase is known from Sri Lanka, Burma, Taiwan, and Thailand. Gemmy crystals come from Alaska, Mexico, Greenland (large yellow transparent crystals), Madagascar, and

Kenya (golden yellow crystals). Transparent adularia occurs in the Alps. Sunstone with reddish reflections caused by fine disseminated hematite or goethite is known from India, the United States (Virginia, Colorado), and Russia (Ural Mts.). Moonstone with a bluish iridescence (orthoclase, microcline, sanidine, and *plagioclase*) is found in Sri Lanka, Burma, India, Australia, Madagascar, and Russia. Micro-

Brilliant cut orthoclases, 23 ct., Madagascar.

Cut adularia, largest stone 25 ct., Sri Lanka.

Amazonite crystals on albite, 180 mm wide, Crystal Park, Colorado.

cline amazonite, the longest used gemstone of all the feldspars, occurs in the United States (Colorado), Russia (Kola Peninsula, Ural Mts), India, Ukraine (Volodarsk Volynskii), and Brazil. Gemmy sani-

Polished amazonite, Kola Peninsula, Russia.

dines come from Sri Lanka (sanidine moonstones), the United States, and Brazil; smoky material has been found in Kenya. Amulets made of amazonite were known from ancient Egypt. An amazonite vase, 22.5 cm high and 14.5 cm in diameter, is in St. Petersburg. The Smithsonian Institution in Washington, D.C., has a cut yellow orthoclase weighing 249.6 ct., a green chatoyant orthoclase weighing 104.5 ct., and a star orthoclase with a white star weighing 22.7 ct., the last two from Sri Lanka. Potassium feldspar gems are mainly of interest to collectors.

Processing: faceted cuts, cabochons, carvings, engravings

Similar minerals: citrine, plagioclase, chalcedony

Imitations: aventurine, glass, synthetic spinel

Identification: hardness, specific gravity, optical methods

Care: Protect potassium feldspars from sudden shocks and sudden temperature changes. Clean in soap and water only; do not use ultrasonic or steam cleaning.

Plagioclase feldspars

NaAlSi$_3$O$_8$ – CaAlSi$_2$O$_8$
From Greek *plagios* + *klasis* = "oblique–cleaving"; from German *Feldspath* – "field spar"

Color: colorless, gray–white, bluish (moonstone, *labradorite*), green, golden yellow (sunstone), reddish • **Diaphaneity:** transparent to translucent, opaque • **Luster:** glassy, pearly • **Fracture:** conchoidal • **Cleavage:** good to poor • **Hardness:** 6–6.5, brittle • **Streak:** white • **Specific gravity:** 2.57–2.77 • **Refractive index:** N_p, N_m, N_g / **Birefringence:** *albite* 1.528, 1.531, 1.538 / 0.011; *oligoclase* 1.529–1.542, 1.543–1.546, 1.547–1.549 / 0.007; *andesine* 1.543, 1.548, 1.551 / 0.008; *labradorite* 1.560, 1.563, 1.568 –1.572 / 0.012; *bytownite* 1.561 –1.567, 1.565 –1.572, 1.570–1.576 / 0.009; *anorthite* 1.576–1.577, 1.583–1.585, 1.589–1.590 / 0.013 • **Dispersion:** 0.012 • **Pleochroism:** none, weak (anorthite, some labradorites) • **Luminescence:** sometimes white, greenish • **Chemistry:** colors caused by hematite, other mineral inclusions • **Special features:** iridescence (moonstone, sunstone), labradorescence, chatoyancy, peacock's–eye effect, aventurescence (some labradorites) • **Treatment:** dark underlay intensifies color

History: Labradorites have long been used for lapidary objects. Other plagioclases have been used only recently and are mainly of interest to collectors.
Chakra: navel
Host rocks: igneous rocks, pegmatites
Occurrences: Nice albites come from Burma, the United States (Virginia – moonstone), Madagascar, Austria, and Switzerland. Gemmy oligoclase is known from Russia (Ural Mts.), Norway (sunstone), the United States, and Kenya. Andesine occurs in the United States (California, Utah), Greenland, Argentina, and South Africa. Mining of labradorite is very widespread. Very famous deposits are located in Canada (Labrador), the United States, Mexico, Australia, and Madagascar. Bytownite is known from Japan, the United States (New Mexico – transparent red), Canada, and Russia. Anorthite oc-

Assorted colors of cut labradorites (sunstone); largest, 10 ct., Oregon.

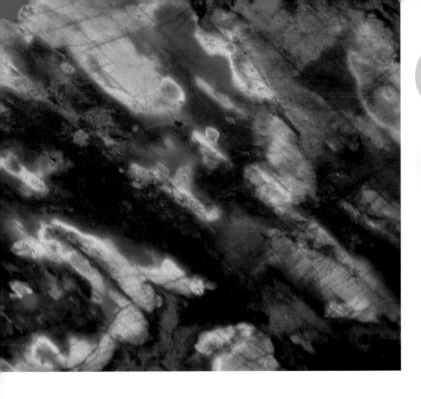

Labradorite polished section, 85 mm wide, Finland. Typical example of labradorescence.

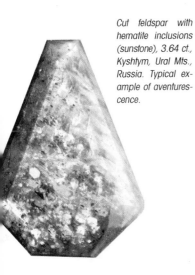

Cut feldspar with hematite inclusions (sunstone), 3.64 ct., Kyshtym, Ural Mts., Russia. Typical example of aventurescence.

curs in India, Japan, the United States (Colorado), Greenland, Finland, and Greece. Multicolored labradorites with reddish reflections come from Finland, and transparent labradorites were found in Mexico (Sonora). Cut albites up to 3 ct. (cat's-eyes up to 10 ct.) and cut labradorites of about 100 ct. are rare. Labradorite gems up to 10–20 ct. are more common, other cut plagioclases reach only about 3–5 ct.

Processing: faceted cuts, cabochons, engravings, table cuts

Similar minerals: orthoclase, bronzite, enstatite, amblygonite

Imitations: aventurine, glass

Identification: hardness, specific gravity, optical methods

Care: Protect plagioclase feldspars from sudden shocks, sudden temperature changes, and acids. Clean in soap and water only; do not use ultrasonic or steam cleaning.

Marcasite

FeS$_2$

From Middle Latin
marcasita – "pyrite"

Color: brass yellow with a greenish tint; often iridescent colors • **Diaphaneity:** opaque • **Luster:** metallic • **Fracture:** conchoidal, uneven • **Cleavage:** indistinct • **Hardness:** 6–6.5 • **Streak:** greenish, black–gray • **Specific gravity:** 4.85–4.9 • **Refractive index:** none • **Dispersion:** none • **Pleochroism:** none • **Luminescence:** none • **Special features:** none • **Treatment:** not known

History: Rarely used as a gemstone, maracasite was popular in the Middle Ages in France, where it appeared in folk jewelry. Small cut marcasites set in silver are now popular in Thailand.
Chakra: throat
Healing effects: energizes; recharge stone in sunlight, then recharge briefly in sunlight
Host rocks: hydrothermal deposits, low –temperature veins, sedimentary rocks
Occurrences: Common in France, Germany, Romania, Pakistan, and Afghanistan, marcasite is also known from many localities in the United States (Illinois), Chile, Mexico, Japan, Russia, Armenia, and Georgia. Very fine druses come from the Czech Republic (Vintířov), although they are not suitable for cutting.
Processing: faceted cuts, rare cabochons; also used in natural shape
Similar minerals: pyrite
Imitations: pyrite
Identification: specific gravity
Care: Protect marcasite from heat or flame perspiration, and acids. Its surface corrodes easily. Clean in warm distilled water and very dilute ammonia; do not use steam cleaning

Druse of marcasite crystals, 66 mm high, Vintířov, Czech Republic.

Pyrite

FeS$_2$

From Latin *pyrites* –
"flint," and Greek *pyr* – "fire," for its ability
to produce sparks when struck

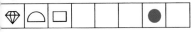

Color: golden yellow; often iridescent colors • **Diaphaneity:** opaque • **Luster:** metallic • **Fracture:** conchoidal, uneven • **Cleavage:** indistinct • **Hardness:** 6–6.5, brittle • **Streak:** black • **Specific gravity:** 5.0–5.03 • **Refractive index:** none • **Dispersion:** none • **Pleochroism:** none • **Luminescence:** none • **Special features:** none • **Treatment:** not known

History: Pyrite has never been considered a very important gemstone. Pyrite jewelry, currently sold under the name marcasite, was popular in ancient Egypt, again in the middle of the 18th century in France, and later during the Victorian era in England.

Chakra: throat

Healing effects: energizes; recharge stone in sunlight, then recharge briefly in sunlight

Host rocks: igneous, metamorphic, and sedimentary rocks, hydrothermal deposits

Occurrences: Good–quality material was once produced in India and Japan. Fine specimens also come from the United States (Tennessee, Colorado, Utah, Pennsylvania, Missouri, Montana), sometimes in crystals up to 12 cm. Pyrite also occurs in Bolivia, Peru, Mexico, Canada, and Australia. Large crystals have been found in Uganda (up to 10 cm), Russia (Dalnegorsk – crystals up to 50 cm), Kazakhstan, and Uzbekistan. In Europe, pyrite occurs in Sweden, Norway, Greece (Xanthe), Spain, Germany, and Italy (Elba – crystals up to 20 cm).

Pyritized ammonite, Litmanová, Slovakia.

Processing: faceted cuts, cabochons, plates; also used in natural shape

Similar minerals: marcasite

Identification: specific gravity

Care: Protect pyrite from heat and acids. Clean in warm distilled water and very dilute ammonia; do not use steam cleaning.

Interpenetration twins of pyrite crystals, cubes up to 50 mm, Navajún, Spain.

Hematite

Fe_2O_3

From Greek *haima*
– "blood," hence "blood red"

History: Although known since Babylonian and ancient Egyptian times, hematite has only rarely been used as a gemstone. It was especially popular in the Middle Ages, when it was set into brooches, rings, bracelets, and seals. Hematite was believed to bring its owner peace and safety.
Astrology: Scorpio
Chakra: base
Healing effects: promotes cell formation; limits bleeding; relieves rheumatism, also insomnia; discharge stone in water, then recharge briefly in sunlight
Host rocks: igneous, metamorphic, and sedimentary rocks, hydrothermal deposits, weathering zones

Color: red–brown, gray–black, black • **Diaphaneity:** rarely translucent, opaque • **Luster:** metallic to dull • **Fracture:** even to conchoidal • **Cleavage:** none • **Hardness:** 5–6.5 (earthy varieties 1), brittle • **Streak:** cherry red • **Specific gravity:** 4.95–5.26 • **Refractive index:** N_e–2.94, N_o–3.22 • **Birefringence:** 0.280 • **Dispersion:** none • **Pleochroism:** weak – brown–red • **Luminescence:** none • **Special features:** none • **Treatment:** not known

Occurrences: Gemmy deposits of this common mineral occur in Arizona, Alaska, and Minnesota. Hematite has also been found in Brazil (Matto Grosso), Venezuela, Canada, Chile, and Cuba. Important deposits are located in Australia (Middleback Range) and New Zealand. Tabular crystals

Contemporary hematite jewelry.

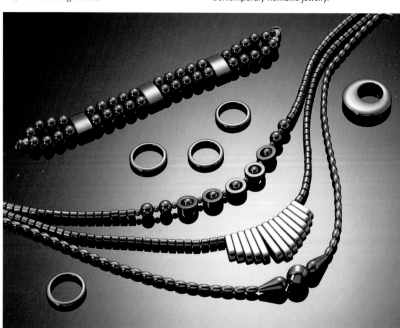

Botryoidal aggregate of hematite, 80 mm wide, Hradiště near Kadaň, Czech Republic.

up to 6 cm wide were found in Japan (Okayama Prefecture).
Hematite also occurs in Russia (Kursk Oblast), Ukraine (Kryvyy Rih), and Kazakhstan. Good–quality material has been found in England (botryoidal aggregates from Cumberland, weighing up to 25 kg), Germany, Switzerland ("alpine roses"), Austria, Italy (nice crystals from Elba), the Czech Republic (Hradiště, Horní Blatná), Spain and France (Puy–de–Dôme, with crystals up to 10 cm).

Processing: faceted cuts, cabochons, beads, table cuts, engravings, carvings
Similar minerals: cassiterite, goethite, psilomelane
Imitations: pressed hematite fragments, synthetic hematite
Identification: hardness, specific gravity, optical methods

Care: Hematite is fragile and should be handled carefully. Protect stones from HCl. There are no cleaning problems unless stone contains inclusions.

Polished section of hematite with jasper (jaspilite), Australia.

Sugilite

$KNa_2(Fe^{2+},Mn^{2+},Al)_2Li_3Si_{12}O_{30}$

After K. Sugi

Color: blue–purple, red–purple, brown–yellow, greenish • **Diaphaneity:** transparent to opaque • **Luster:** glassy • **Fracture:** conchoidal • **Cleavage:** none • **Hardness:** 6–6.5 • **Streak:** white • **Specific gravity:** 2.74 • **Refractive index:** N_e–1.607, N_o–1.610 • **Birefringence:** 0.003–0.005 • **Dispersion:** none • **Pleochroism:** none • **Luminescence:** none • **Chemistry:** color caused by trace amounts of Mn • **Special features:** none • **Treatment:** not known

History: Discovered in 1944, sugilite has been used as a gemstone only in the last few decades.

Chakra: crown

Healing effects: promotes positive thinking; used to treat ailments of liver, gallbladder; discharge stone in lukewarm water, then recharge briefly in sunlight

Host rocks: alkaline igneous rocks

Occurrences: A very rare mineral associated with albite, aegirine, and pectolite, sugilite was first discovered on Iwagi Island, Japan. Nice purple sugilites were later found in Namibia and South Africa (Cape Province, Wessels Mine). It also comes from India (Madhya Pradesh). Fac-

eted cut stones up to a few carats are marketed under the name **Royal Azel**. The largest known sugilite gem, almost transparent, weighs 23.5 ct. and is preserved at the Smithsonian Institution in Washington, D.C.

Sugilite polished section, Namibia.

Intarsia using sugilite, malachite, turquoise, azurite, gold, and diamonds, by Jim Kaufman, United States.

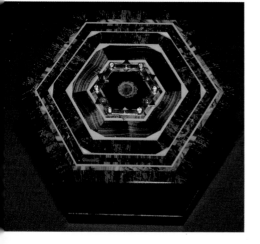

Processing: cabochons, faceted cuts, engravings, intarsia

Similar minerals: charoite, stichtite

Imitations: not known

Identification: hardness, specific gravity, optical methods

Care: Sugilite is fragile and should be handled carefully. Protect stones from HF. Clean in soap and water only; do not use ultrasonic or steam cleaning.

Charoite

(K,Sr,Ba)(Ca,Na)₂(Si,Al)₄O₁₀(OH,F)

After Chara River, Siberia

◠	▢	🐎		◐	

History: A new gemstone, charoite has been used for lapidary objects only since the late 1950s.

Host rocks: alkaline igneous rocks

Occurrences: Charoite is found only at its type locality, Murun Massif, Yakutia, where it occurs in dikes and lenslike bodies in alkaline syenites over an area of about 10 km² (4 mi²). The material is almost monomineral (90% – charoite; 10% – dark green aegirine, yellow tinaksite, green–white nepheline, and scattered grains of ore minerals). Stones with a fibrous, radial texture and silky luster are most popular; a pearly luster is much rarer.

Processing: cabochons, carvings, table cuts

Similar minerals: sugilite

Imitations: not known

Identification: hardness, specific gravity, optical methods

Care: Protect charoite from sudden shocks and abrasion. Clean in warm water.

Color: light to dark purple; sometimes blue–purple • **Diaphaneity:** translucent, opaque • **Luster:** glassy, silky • **Fracture:** splintery • **Cleavage:** indistinct • **Hardness:** 5–6 • **Streak:** white • **Specific gravity:** 2.54–2.68 • **Refractive index:** N_p–1.550, N_m–1.553, N_g–1.559 • **Birefringence:** 0.009 • **Dispersion:** none • **Pleochroism:** distinct – pink, colorless • **Luminescence:** none • **Chemistry:** trace amounts of Ba, Sr • **Special features:** chatoyancy • **Treatment:** not known

6

Charoite vase, 300 mm high, contemporary Russian work.

Charoite, Chara River, Russia.

Diopside

$CaMgS_2O_6$
From Greek *di + opsis* = "two
–appearance" because crystals
often have two sets of prism faces

History: Although an important rock–forming mineral, formally described in 1800, diopside is only rarely used as a gemstone.
Host rocks: igneous and metamorphic rocks, placers
Occurrences: Gemmy diopside comes from Sri Lanka (Balangoda and Ratnapura regions), Burma (yellow and green stones with cat's–eye effect), and India (black star diopside). It also occurs in Pakistan (Hunza region, with cat's–eye effect), Iran, the United States (Connecticut, New York, California, and Illinois), and Canada (Quebec, Ontario). Nice gem–quality material comes from Brazil; green crystals with a cat's–eye effect were found in Australia and Kenya (Kwale region). Diopside is also known from Russia (Ural Mts., Lake Baikal), Uzbekistan, Italy, Austria (white with cat's–eye effect), Sweden, and Finland. Beautiful gemmy diopsides have recently come from the Merelani Hills of Tanzania. The Smithsonian Institution in Washington, D.C., preserves a fine black star and a cat's–eye

Diopsides from various localities; largest cut stone, 11 ct.; crystal from Sludyanka, Russia.

Color: yellow, green to emerald green (chrome diopside), green–black, gray, colorless, white, purple (*violane*), brown; rarely blue • **Diaphaneity:** transparent, translucent • **Luster:** glassy • **Fracture:** uneven to conchoidal • **Cleavage:** perfect • **Hardness:** 5.5–6.5, brittle • **Streak:** white • **Specific gravity:** 3.22–3.31 • **Refractive index:** N_p–1.664–1.695, N_m–1.672–1.701, N_g–1.695–1.721 • **Birefringence:** 0.024–0.035 • **Dispersion:** none • **Pleochroism:** none, very weak – gray–green, yellow green, light green • **Luminescence:** sometimes green–white, creamy, blue • **Chemistry:** color caused by trace amounts of Cr^{3+}, Fe^{2+}, Fe^{3+} • **Special features:** asterism • **Treatment:** not known

Star diopsides; largest, 20 ct., India.

diopside from India (133 and 24.1 ct.), a green diopside from Madagascar (19.2 ct.), and a yellow diopside from Italy (6.8 ct.).
Processing: faceted cuts, cabochons
Similar minerals: hiddenite, olivine
Imitations: not known
Identification: hardness, specific gravity, optical methods
Care: Protect diopside's perfect cleavage from sudden shocks and sudden temperature changes. Clean in soap and water only; do not use ultrasonic or steam cleaning.

Chrome diopside

(diopside variety)

$CaMgSi_2O_6$

After Cr impurity in diopside

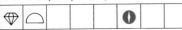

Color: emerald green • **Diaphaneity:** transparent, translucent • **Luster:** glassy • **Fracture:** uneven to conchoidal • **Cleavage:** perfect • **Hardness:** 5.5–6.5, brittle • **Streak:** white • **Specific gravity:** 3.17–3.32 • **Refractive index:** N_p–1.669–1.674, N_m–1.680, N_g–1.698–1.702 • **Birefringence:** 0.028 • **Dispersion:** none • **Pleochroism:** visible • **Luminescence:** creamy • **Chemistry:** color caused by trace amounts of Cr • **Special features:** rare chatoyancy • **Treatment:** not known

History: Only recently used as a gemstone, chrome diopside is gaining in popularity.

Host rocks: igneous and metamorphic rocks

Occurrences: Chrome diopside occurs in ultrabasic rocks; crystals are rare, up to 10 cm. Some of the most beautiful chrome diopside comes from the Inagli Massif in Siberia, Russia (sometimes called "**Siberian emerald**"); smaller sources are known from the Ural Mts. It has also been found in Cuba, Mexico, and Brazil (Malacacheta region). Other localities are in Kenya (Kwale region), Madagascar, New Zealand, Australia, and Japan (Akita Prefecture). Very fine chrome diopsides come from Finland (Outokumpu), and smaller pieces are known from Romania.

Chrome diopside; cut stones, 4 ct., Inagli Massif, Russia.

Processing: faceted cuts, cabochons

Similar minerals: demantoid, emerald, uvarovite

Imitations: glass

Identification: hardness, specific gravity, optical methods

Care: Protect chrome diopside's perfect cleavage from sudden shocks and sudden temperature changes. Clean in soap and water only; do not use ultrasonic or steam cleaning.

Rhodonite

$(Mn^{2+}, Fe^{2+}, Mg, Ca)SiO_3$

From Greek *rhodon*
– "rose," hence "pink, red"

History: Although not formally described until 1819, rhodonite has long been used to make lapidary objects, vases, and sarcophagi. During the 16th century, it was considered to be a stone of happiness, joy, and honor, and was believed to possess magical powers.
Astrology: birthstone for Aries
Chakra: heart
Healing effects: strengthens mind; restores memory; heals blood vessels; discharge stone in naturally soft water, then briefly recharge in sunlight
Host rocks: metamorphic rocks, hydrothermal deposits
Occurrences: Remarkable clear crystals are known from Franklin and Sterling Hill in New Jersey, historically the most important producer of rhodonite, which also occurs in California, Montana, and Alaska, and has been found in Canada, Brazil (Ouro Preto, Minas Gerais), and Mexico. Although very fine crystals occur in Peru (Huanzala), the

Color: pink, meat red, raspberry red, red–brown, red; often with black veinlets of Mn oxides • **Diaphaneity:** transparent to opaque • **Luster:** glassy, dull • **Fracture:** conchoidal • **Cleavage:** perfect • **Hardness:** 5.5.–6.5, brittle • **Streak:** white • **Specific gravity:** 3.57–3.68 • **Refractive index:** N_p–1.711–1.738, N_m–1.716–1.741, N_g–1.724–1.751 • **Birefringence:** 0.011–0.014 • **Dispersion:** none • **Pleochroism:** weak to distinct – orange–pink • **Luminescence:** sometimes dark red, pink • **Chemistry:** color caused by trace amounts of Mn • **Special features:** common Mn–oxide dendrites • **Treatment:** not known

world's finest transparent crystals, up to 10 cm, come from Australia (Broken Hill) yielding raw material for faceted stones up to several carats. Other occurrences are in Japan (Honshu Island), Indonesia, and India. Nice red crystals were found in Tanzania (Mwembe), Madagascar, South Africa and

Rhodonite crystals, 80 mm wide.

Lapidary objects made of rhodonite. Box is contemporary Russian work, 110 mm wide.

Algeria. Very important deposits are in Russia (Ural Mts.), where rhodonite mining started in the 18th century and where monoliths up to 40 t (44 short tons) have been found; the best–known deposit was Maloye Sedelnikovo. Other deposits have been found in Kazakhstan, Uzbekistan, and Ukraine. Gemmy rhodonite occurs in Sweden (Pajsberg, Langban) and Spain. Smaller localities are known from Slovakia, the Czech Republic (Chvaletice), Germany, Italy, Romania, and France. Decorative lapidary rhodonite objects are among the highlights of many museum collections. A very large rhodonite bowl, 88 cm high and 185 cm in diameter, made in 1867, is preserved at the Hermitage in St. Petersburg. Weighing 7 t (7.7 short tons), the sarcophagus for Czar Alexander II's wife was made of rhodonite in 1905 and can be seen at St. Peter and Paul Cathedral in St. Petersburg. Beautiful chandeliers, vases, lamps, bowls, cups, ashtrays, and paperweights were also made of rhodonite at the same time. Rhodonite facing was used at the Mayakovski Station of the Moscow Metro and in the Congress Hall of the Kremlin. Rhodonite suitable for faceting is very rare, and cut stones only reach about 2–3 ct.

Processing: faceted cuts, cabochons, lapidary objects, facing, carvings, glyptics
Similar minerals: rhodochrosite, thulite
Identification: specific gravity, hardness, optical methods
Care: Protect rhodonite from shocks, temperature changes, heat or flame, and abrasion. Clean in soap and water only; do not use ultrasonic or steam cleaning.

Rhodonite, Maloye Sedelnikovo, Russia.

Opal

$SiO_2 \cdot nH_2O$

From Sanskrit *upala* – "stone, jewel"

6

History: Known to the ancient Assyrians, Babylonians, and Romans, opal was first used to make tools and only later to make decorative objects and jewelry. Precious opal, described by Pliny the Elder, comes from Dubník, Slovakia, the oldest known precious opal deposit in the world, and was long thought to ward off misfortune and troubles.

Astrology: birthstone for Capricorn

Chakra: crown

Healing effects: relieves melancholy; calms nerves; strengthens heart; sharpens eyesight; used to treat stomach, intestinal problems; discharge stone in water, then recharge briefly in sunlight

Host rocks: volcanic rocks, weathering zones, sedimentary rocks

Occurrences: Opal is found the world over. Common and wooden opals occur in India, Mongolia, Indonesia, Iraq, Syria, and Australia. Wooden opals, forming whole petrified forests, are very popular and attractive. Petrified wood is known from Ne-

Color: Brown, yellow–brown, brown–black (***common opal***), red, brown–red ("***meat opal***"), green, yellow–green (***prase opal***), colorless (***hyalite***), white (***milky opal, cachalong***), orange–red, iridescent (***precious opal***); different textures include massive, ball-shaped, and banded (***wooden opal***). Color dulls after stone loses absorbed water (***hydrophane***) and is sometimes caused by inclusions of other minerals (***moss opal***). • **Diaphaneity:** transparent to opaque • **Luster:** glassy, greasy, pearly • **Fracture:** conchoidal • **Cleavage:** none • **Hardness:** 5.5.–6.5 • **Streak:** white, yellowish, brownish • **Specific gravity:** 1.98–2.25, it increases from hyalite to wooden and common opals • **Refractive index:** N–1.44–1.47 • **Birefringence:** none • **Dispersion:** none or very little • **Pleochroism:** none • **Luminescence:** sometimes greenish, yellowish or none • **Chemistry:** color caused by trace amounts of Ni, Cr, Fe, Mn, inclusions of other minerals • **Special features:** opalescence, iridescence, chatoyancy • **Treatment:** proofing with different colored solutions

Nodule of common opal in matrix, Nová Ves near Oslavany, Czech Republic.

Common opal, United States.

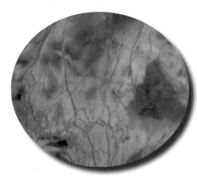

Dendritic opal, *United States.*

Dendritic opal, Křemže, Czech Republic.

Wooden opal, Lubietová, Slovakia.

"Meat opal," Herlany, Slovakia.

vada, Wyoming, Colorado, Oregon, Washington, Mexico (Hidalgo and San Luis Potosí), Argentina (Patagonia), Brazil, Ecuador (green–white opals), and Peru. Large opal deposits are known from Russia, Kyrgystan, Ukraine, Georgia, Armenia. Colored opals of good quality have also been found in Egypt and Uganda. Wooden and common opals are abundant in Slovakia

Botryoidal aggregate of hyalite, 35 mm wide, Valeč, Czech Republic.

Fire opal *pebbles, 5 mm, Mexico.*

(more than 100 localities), the Czech Republic, Hungary, Romania, Serbia, Macedonia, Poland, Ireland, France, and Bulgaria (petrified forest on Black Sea). India the United States (Nevada, Oregon), Russia (Kamchatka), and the Czech Republic also produce moss opals, while Slovakia produces meat opals. Hyalite is commonly associated with precious opals, but sometimes also forms typical botryoidal aggregates in stones from the Czech Republic (Valeč), Japan (Takayama), the United States (Oregon, Wyoming, Nevada), Mexico (San Luis Potosí), New Zealand, and Faroe Islands. Prase opal is known from the United States (Nevada) Brazil (Bahía), Australia (Tasmania), New Caledonia, Tanzania, Serbia (Golesh), and Poland. The most valuable opals are, of course, precious opals. At present 80–90% of the world's production comes from Australia; precious opals occur in the weathering zones of Queensland, New South Wales, Victoria, Southern and Western Australia. One of the richest deposits in Yowah, Queensland, yields white to

Precious opal, 65.21 ct., Australia.

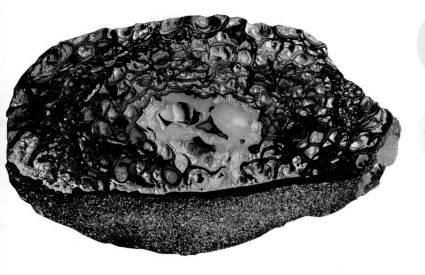

"Matrix opal," 65 mm wide, Bull's Creek, Queensland, Australia.

Precious opal doublets, 10 mm, Australia.

blue–white opals with blue, green, and red color changes. Large concentrations of opal are known from Southern Australia (Coober Pedy vicinity), where opals in kaolinized sands, forming veinlets and

nests and petrifying flora and fauna, occur in an area of about 180 km^2 (70 mi^2). Precious opals from the vicinity of Andamooka come from siliceous sandstones and are often black. Black opals with green, blue, yellow, and red color changes have been found at Lightning Ridge, New South Wales. Precious opals are also known from Indonesia (Java) and India (Hyderabad). More important localities are in Nevada (Virgin Valley), where precious opal with red and orange color changes fills in the cracks in wooden opals. "Star opals" in rhyolites have been found in Idaho, and yellowish, greenish, and colorless opals occur in Oregon. Wooden opals with a slight color change have also been found in Yellowstone National Park (Wyoming). Smaller occurrences are known from New Mexico, Washington, and Texas. Mexico is one of the most important producers of red, bluish, greenish, rarely black precious and fire

Gold pendant with precious opal, rubies, and pearl. Work of jewelers' school in Turnov, Czech Republic, beginning of 20th century.

Fire opal, 30 mm wide, Jalisco, Mexico.

Gold necklace with fire opals, agates, pearls and diamonds, by Gilbert Albert, Geneva, Switzerland.

opals, including the girasol variety, with some 150 known localities (Querétaro, Hidalgo, Chihuahua, and Jalisco). Bluish, greenish, red, and orange precious opals have recently been found in Brazil (Piauí), where they occur in Devonian sandstones. Fire opals are also known from Brazil (Ceará), with smaller localities in Honduras and Guatemala. Zimbabwe, South Africa, and Russia (Chukotka and Kamchatka) produce some precious opals; a smaller deposit occurs in Ukraine. Fire opals come from Kazakhstan (Kara–Agach). World–famous precious opals from Slovakia (Dubník) opals are white with a beautiful color change (blue, red and green). Many opals are famous for their unique color, shape, or size. The Harlequin (600 g), which comes from Dubník, is on display at the Natural History Museum in Vienna. Other well–known stones are the Devonshire, measuring 5 x 2.5 cm (100 ct.), the Olympic Australis (3.6 kg), the Light of the World (512 g), and the Roebling (608 g). The Smithsonian Institution in Washington, D.C., preserves a black opal from Nevada (355 ct.), an orange opal from Mexico (143.2 ct.), and white opals from Australia (345, 155, and 83 ct.).

Processing: faceted cuts, cabochons, doublets, triplets, carvings, engravings

Similar minerals: agate, hyacinth, onyx, chrysoprase, ivory, howlite

Imitations: synthetic opal, glass

Identification: hardness, specific gravity, optical methods

Care: Protect opal from sudden shocks, sudden temperature changes, and abrasion. Clean in soap and water only; do not use ultrasonic or steam cleaning.

Gold ring with precious opals and pink pearl, by Karel Valter, Geneva, Switzerland.

Sodalite

$Na_8Al_6Si_6O_{24}Cl_2$

After chemical composition

History: Formally described in 1807, sodalite was believed to clear the mind, preparing it for intuitive knowledge and thus for deep thinking. It has the color of a night sky.

Astrology: birthstone for Virgo

Chakra: forehead

Healing effects: calms emotions; lowers blood pressure; discharge stone in water, then recharge briefly in sunlight

Host rocks: igneous rocks (nepheline syenites), metamorphic calcareous rocks

Occurrences: Fine sodalites come from Burma and India (Rajasthan). Smaller oc-

Color: colorless, blue, green; rarely light pink (*hackmanite*) • **Diaphaneity:** transparent to translucent, opaque • **Luster:** glassy, greasy • **Fracture:** uneven to conchoidal • **Cleavage:** poor • **Hardness:** 5.5–6, brittle • **Streak:** white, bluish • **Specific gravity:** 2.14–2.40 • **Birefringence:** none • **Dispersion:** 0.018 • **Pleochroism:** none • **Luminescence:** sometimes orange to purple • **Chemistry:** hackmanite (pink) is rich in S • **Special features:** none • **Treatment:** not known

currences are known from Korea. It is also reported from Angola, Namibia (Gopogo – transparent sodalite), Guinea, South

Sodalite polished section, 80 mm wide, Canada.

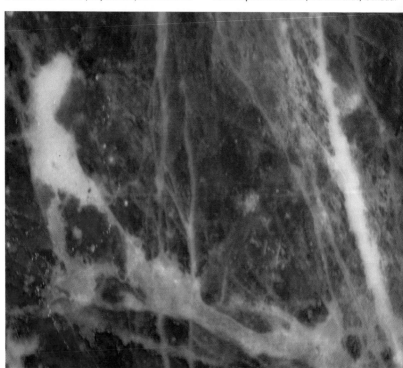

Sodalite lapidary objects, used in healing.

Africa (Transvaal). The United States has produced sodalite from Maine, Montana, Arkansas, South Dakota, Colorado, New Hampshire, and New Jersey. At present, Canada has the most important deposits, in Ontario (Bancroft and Dungannon – "blue stone"); other localities are in British Columbia and Quebec. Sodalite also occurs in Greenland, Brazil (Bahía), and Bolivia. Famous deposits were mined in Russia (Ural Mts., Kola Peninsula), with other occurrences in Tajikistan. In Europe, small deposits are known from Germany, Italy, Scotland, Romania (Ditrau Massif), Portugal, and Norway.

Processing: cabochons, engravings, carvings, faceted cuts (rare)

Similar minerals: dumortierite, hauyne, lazurite, azurite

Imitations: glass

Identification: hardness, specific gravity, optical methods

Care: Protect sodalite from sudden shocks, abrasion, and HF. Clean in soap and water only; do not use ultrasonic or steam cleaning. Pink stones fade in light.

Sodalite polished section, Canada.

Scapolite
(*marialite–meionite* series)

$3NaAlSi_3O_8.NaCl - 3CaAl_2Si_2O_8.CaCO_3$

From Latin *scapus* + Greek *lithos* = "shaft stone" for crystal shape

History: Although formally described in 1800, scapolite has rarely been used as a gemstone, and only in recent times.

Host rocks: metamorphic rocks, pneumatolytic deposits

Occurrences: Scapolite, often of gem quality, is relatively common. Important occur-

Scapolites from various localities. Yellow cut stones (largest, 35 ct.) are from Tanzania; purple from Pamir Mts., Tajikistan; crystals from Brazil.

Color: colorless, white gray, green–gray, bluish, pink, purple, green–yellow, brown, orange • **Diaphaneity:** transparent, translucent • **Luster:** glassy, silky, pearly on cleavage planes • **Fracture:** uneven to conchoidal • **Cleavage:** good • **Hardness:** 5–6, brittle • **Streak:** white • **Specific gravity:** 2.50–2.62 (marialite), 2.78 (meionite) • **Refractive index:** N_e–1.540–1.548, N_o–1.549–1.567 • **Birefringence:** 0.007–0.020 • **Dispersion:** 0.017 • **Pleochroism:** visible to naked eye • **Luminescence:** sometimes yellow to orange • **Chemistry:** color caused by trace amounts of SO_3 (blue), Cr (purple and pink) • **Special features:** chatoyancy • **Treatment:** irradiation

Scapolite, crystal 25 mm long, Kunrun Mts., Xinjiang Autonomous Region, China.

...rences are in Burma (Mogok region), where yellow, pink, purple, and blue crystals were found (some with cat's–eye effect). Similar scapolites also come from Sri Lanka (Ratnapura and Balangoda regions). Yellow scapolites have been found in Canada (Quebec, Ontario) and light yellow transparent crystals, up to 40 x 10 cm, in Brazil (Bahía and Espírito Santo). Light yellow, pink, and purple gemmy scapolites occur in Tanzania, sometimes with a cat's–eye effect (Umba River region). Similar stones have been found in Kenya (also bluish), Madagascar, and Mozambique (purple). Purple scapolites now come from China, often with a cat's–eye effect. Russia has produced some scapolites from Sludyanka; colorless, yellow, and purple scapolites have been found in Tajikistan. Large crystals are known from Finland, Sweden, Norway, and Italy (colorless marialites). Large cut stones are rare, although the Smithsonian Institution in Washington, D.C., preserves a colorless cut stone and a cat's–eye from Burma (288 and 29.9 ct.), and a yellow–orange cut stone from Tanzania (103.4 ct.).

Processing: faceted cuts, cabochons

Similar minerals: heliodor, topaz, quartz, amblygonite

Imitations: glass, quartz

Identification: hardness, specific gravity, optical methods

Care: Protect scapolite from sudden shocks, temperature changes, heat or flame, abrasion, and acids. Clean in soap and water only. Irradiated stones may fade in light.

Lazurite (lapis lazuli)

$(Na,Ca)_{7-8}(Al,Si)_{12}(O,S)_{24}/$
$(SO_4),Cl_2,(OH)_2/$

From Persian *lazhuward*
– "sky blue, azure"

History: Most commonly referred to as lapis lazuli, lazurite has been known for more than 7,000 years. Small lazurite lapidary objects were found in the Egyptian pyramids; it was used by the Babylonians and a symbol of power to the ancient Chinese. The Greeks and the Romans made figurines, amulets, bowls, and sealing sticks out of it. Until synthesized in 1828, the pigment ultramarine was made from powdered lazurite mixed with wax and oil.
Astrology: birthstone for Virgo
Chakra: forehead
Healing effects: relieves headaches; lowers blood pressure, temperature; reduces pain during menstruation; when heated, used to treat inflammations and swellings; discharge stone in soft water, then recharge briefly in sunlight
Host rocks: contact metamorphic rocks
Occurrences: The most important and longest mined deposits are in Afghanistan. Lazurite has been mined since antiquity in Badakhshan region, on the upper

Color: dark blue, blue–green, light blue; often with pyrite impregnations • **Diaphaneity:** opaque, rarely translucent • **Luster:** dull • **Fracture:** uneven • **Cleavage:** indistinct • **Hardness:** 5–6, brittle • **Streak:** light blue • **Specific gravity:** 2.38–2.45 (for mineral), 2.7–2.9 (for rock, consisting mostly of lazurite) • **Refractive index:** N–1.500–1.522 • **Birefringence:** none • **Dispersion:** none • **Pleochroism:** none • **Luminescence:** sometimes orange–red, light pink, white • **Chemistry:** color caused by inclusions • **Special features:** common pyrite impregnations • **Treatment:** proofing, often combined with dyeing

part of the Amudarya River, first reported by Marco Polo in the 13th century. The Sar–e–Sang deposit is located at an elevation of 3,000–4,000 m (9,800–13,100 ft) and covers an area of about 2 km² (0.75 mi²). Blocks weighing up to 110 kg have been found there, although crystals, up to 5 cm are rare. Smaller occurrences are known from Pakistan (Skardu region), Burma (Dattan Valley), and India (Kashmir and Madhya Pradesh). World–famous Russian lazurite was discovered in 1851 near Lake Baikal, where 8 localities are known and dark blue lazurite blocks weigh up to 60 kg and in 1930 in Tajikistan (Pamir Mts.). Pamir lazurite is found at an elevation o

Lazurite polished section with pyrite, Afghanistan.

Lazurite, Chile.

Lapis lazuli rosary, height of medallion 70 mm, made in Prague after 1600.

4,500 m (14,800 ft), including weakly pyritized aggregates up to 5 m. Lazurite is also known from South Africa, Angola, and Rwanda (Buranda pegmatites). Chile is also an important producer of light blue to green–blue lazurite, which is mined at an elevation of 3,000 m (9,850 ft) in Coquimbo and Aconcagua Provinces. Smaller localities are also in the United States (Colorado, California, and Wyoming). Many lazurite lapidary objects are in museums and treasuries all over the world. Probably the best–known objects are the lazurite columns in the St. Isaac Cathedral and the lazurite objects at the Hermitage, both in St. Petersburg, and a blue lazurite vase, 40.5 cm high, at the Palazzo Pitti in Florence, Italy.

Processing: cabochons, faceted cuts, table cuts, small to large glyptics, facings
Similar minerals: sodalite, hauyne, nosean, lazulite

Imitations: "Swiss" or "German lazulite" (artificially dyed jasper), synthetic spinel, synthetic Gilson lazurite
Identification: hardness, specific gravity, optical methods
Care: Protect lazurite from sudden temperature changes, abrasion, and acids. Clean in soap and water only; do not use ultrasonic or steam cleaning.

Lazulite *polished section (lazulite is often confused with lazurite), Stickelberg, Austria.*

Amblygonite

$(Li,Na)Al(PO_4)(F,OH)$
From Greek *amblys* + *gonia*
= "obtuse–angled" for crystal shape

Color: colorless, white, yellow, gray, blue, green, light purple, pink • **Diaphaneity:** transparent, translucent • **Luster:** glassy, greasy, pearly on cleavage planes • **Fracture:** uneven to conchoidal • **Cleavage:** perfect, good • **Hardness:** 5.5–6, brittle • **Streak:** white • **Specific gravity:** 2.98–3.11 • **Refractive index:** N_p–1.611, N_m–1.622, N_g–1.637 • **Birefringence:** 0.022 • **Dispersion:** 0.020 • **Pleochroism:** none • **Luminescence:** sometimes orange, bluish • **Chemistry:** soluble in acids • **Special features:** none • **Treatment:** not known

History: Formally described in 1817, amblygonite has rarely been used as a gemstone, and only in recent times.

Host rocks: pegmatites, metasomatic rocks

Occurrences: Nice gemmy amblygonites come from Burma, Kazakhstan, and Australia, purple stones from Namibia, and dark brown stones from Kenya. Fine amblygonites have been found in the United States (Maine, South Dakota, California) and Brazil (Minas Gerais). Amblygonite also occurs in Europe (Germany, Sweden, France, Spain), but not of gem quality. Gems are usually small (up to 15 ct.) and rarely reach 70 ct. (mostly from Brazil). The Smithsonian

Amblygonite crystal, 60 mm wide, Linópolis, Minas Gerais, Brazil.

Cut amblygonites, 3–4 ct., Galilea, Minas Gerais, Brazil.

Institution in Washington, D.C., has a yellow cut amblygonite from Brazil (62.5 ct.) and another from Burma (19.7 ct.).

Processing: faceted cuts, cabochons

Similar minerals: brazilianite, citrine, heliodor

Imitations: glass

Identification: hardness, specific gravity, optical methods

Care: Protect amblygonite from sudden shocks, sudden temperature changes, abrasion, and acids. Clean in soap and water only; do not use ultrasonic or steam cleaning.

Brazilianite

NaAl₃(PO₄)₂(OH)₄

After Brazil

$NaAl_3(PO_4)_2(OH)_4$

History: Originally mistaken for chrysoberyl, brazilianite was determined to be a new mineral by Frederick Pough and E. P. Henderson in 1945.

Host rocks: pegmatites

Occurrences: Brazilianite is known from pegmatites in Minas Gerais, Brazil, where it forms crystals up to 20 cm, and also in Espírito Santo and Paraíba, with smaller occurrences in New Hampshire and Maine. Brazilianite has been found in Dolní Bory (Czech Republic), but it is not of gem quality. Cut stones rarely exceed 10 ct. The American Museum of Natural History in New York has a brilliant cut gem weighing

Druse of brazilianite crystals, Corrego Frío Mine, Divino Das Laranjeiras, Minas Gerais, Brazil.

Color: colorless, light yellow, yellow–green, light green • **Diaphaneity:** transparent • **Luster:** glassy • **Fracture:** conchoidal • **Cleavage:** good • **Hardness:** 5.5 • **Streak:** white • **Specific gravity:** 2.98–3.0 • **Refractive index:** N_p–1.602, N_m–1.609, N_g–1.623 • **Birefringence:** 0.019–0.021 • **Dispersion:** 0.014 • **Pleochroism:** weak, depending on color • **Luminescence:** none • **Chemistry:** primary pegmatite phosphate • **Special features:** none • **Treatment:** not known

19 ct. and an emerald cut gem weighing 23 ct.

Processing: faceted cuts, cabochons (rare)

Similar minerals: chrysoberyl, topaz, heliodor, apatite, amblygonite

Imitations: glass, quartz

Identification: hardness, specific gravity, optical methods

Care: Protect brazilianite from sudden shocks, sudden temperature changes, abrasion, and acids. Clean in soap and water only; do not use ultrasonic or steam cleaning.

Turquoise

$Cu^{2+}Al_6(PO_4)_4(OH)_8 \cdot 4H_2O$

From French (*pierre*) *turquoise*
– "Turkish (stone)" because
it was first brought from Persia via Turkey

Color: blue, green–blue, apple green, light brown • **Diaphaneity:** opaque, rarely translucent in small crystals • **Luster:** dull, greasy, glassy (crystals) • **Fracture:** even, conchoidal • **Cleavage:** none • **Hardness:** 5–6 • **Streak:** white, bluish • **Specific gravity:** 2.6–2.9 • **Refractive index:** N_p–1.61, N_m–1.62, N_g–1.65 • **Birefringence:** 0.040 • **Dispersion:** none • **Pleochroism:** weak – colorless, light blue • **Luminescence:** green–yellow, light blue • **Chemistry:** color caused by trace amounts of Fe^{2+}, Fe^{3+} • **Special features:** common Fe–oxide (limonite) dendrites ("***spider web***") • **Treatment:** proofing with different dyes and bonding agents

History: Highly valued by the Aztecs, Egyptians, Tibetans, and later by the Ottomans, turquoise has long been used to make vases, rings, brooches, bracelets, and other jewelry. It was considered a stone of happiness in the Orient and believed to protect its owner from snakebite.

Astrology: birthstone for Pisces, Sagittarius (Babylonians)

Chakra: throat

Healing effects: used to treat ailments of nose, throat, lungs; strengthens heart; sharpens eyesight; discharge stone in water, then briefly recharge in sunlight

Host rocks: faulted veins in sedimentary rocks

Occurrences: The most famous historical deposits are in Iran (formerly Persia) near Nishapur, where turquoise of the finest quality (associated with kaolinized and silicified trachytes, locally brecciated) has been mined for more than 4,000 years. Started as a surface operation, extensive mining now takes place 100 m below the surface. Another important historical source is China (Manchuria, Sichuan Province), where Marco Polo first reported turquoise. Small occurrences are located in Tibet, India, Afghanistan, Turkey, Chile,

Turquoise nodule, 65 mm wide, Kazakhstan.

*Popular substitutes for turquoise, white **howlite** and **magnesite** dyed blue.*

Peru, Brazil, and Mexico. American Indians mined turquoise in over 35 localities (New Mexico, Colorado, Nevada), the largest piece from Nevada weighing 80 kg. Smaller deposits are also in California and Arizona. Australian turquoise is known from New South Wales (Bodalla), Victoria, and Queensland. Historically important deposits (associated with azurite, malachite, and chrysocolla) have been mined in Egypt (Sinai Peninsula) for 3,000 years over an area of 640 km^2 (250 mi^2). Smaller African localities are in Ethiopia, Namibia, Sudan, and Tanzania. Old deposits are known from Russia (Polar Urals); also from Uzbekistan and Kazakhstan, where turquoise has been mined for 2,000 years over an area of 300 km^2 (120 mi^2). Other occurrences are in Armenia, Bulgaria, the United Kingdom, Poland, and Germany.

Processing: cabochons, table cuts, small to medium glyptics

Similar minerals: lazulite, lazurite, malachite, chrysocolla

Imitations: glass, enamel, ceramics, plastic, porcelain, synthetic turquoise, bone turquoise, dyed howlite and magnesite

Identification: hardness, specific gravity, optical methods

Care: Protect turquoise from sudden temperature changes, abrasion, perspiration, acids, soaps, and detergents. Clean in distilled water with wetting agent. To remove oils and grease, soak overnight in alcohol. Do not use ultrasonic or steam cleaning. Stones may fade in light; cosmetics and perspiration may cause color to change from blue to green.

Turquoise, Anatolia, Turkey.

Apatite

$Ca_5(PO_4)_3(OH,F,Cl)$

From Greek *apate* – "deceit" –
it was mistaken for other stones

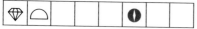

History: Formally described in 1842, apatite has been often confused with other stones. It is mainly of interest to collectors.

Host rocks: pegmatites, pneumatolytic deposits, hydrothermal deposits, sedimentary rocks, placers

Occurrences: Colorless, light blue or green, rarely chatoyant apatites occur in Burma (Mogok region). Blue (often chatoyant), green, and yellow stones come from Sri Lanka, green, chatoyant stones from India, and attractive red stones from Pakistan (Nasart region). Brazil is a very important producer of blue, green, and rarely light pink gemmy apatites (Morro Velho), gray crystals up to 10 cm (Urupucá region), bluish fluorapatites (Virgem da Lapa region), and olive green apatites (Campo Linda). Purple crystals up to 25 cm and cut stones up to 170 ct. are known from Maine, purple, pink–red, and green crystals from California, brown–green crystals up to

Color: colorless, yellow–green (**asparagus stone**), yellow, green, blue–green, purple, red, brown–red; sometimes multicolored • **Diaphaneity:** transparent, translucent • **Luster:** glassy • **Fracture:** conchoidal to uneven • **Cleavage:** poor • **Hardness:** 5, brittle • **Streak:** white • **Specific gravity:** 3.10–3.35 • **Refractive index:** N_e–1.633, N_o–1.636 • **Birefringence:** 0.001–0.013 • **Dispersion:** 0.013 • **Pleochroism:** distinct, visibly dichroic (bluish varieties) • **Luminescence:** yellow, yellow–orange, pink, light green, blue, white • **Chemistry:** trace amounts of Cl (*chlorapatite*), F (*fluorapatite*), Sr, REE, Si, Ca, Mn • **Special features:** chatoyancy • **Treatment:** not known

10 cm from Alaska, and indigo blue apatites from South Dakota. Yellow or yellow–green crystals and cut stones up to 30 ct. occur in Mexico, while Bolivia has produced pink and colorless apatites. East Africa has long been a prolific source,

Cut apatite, 10.5 ct., arranged on a matrix with embedded crystals, Sludyanka, Russia.

Fluorapatite druse; crystal, 20 mm long, Cerro Mercado, Durango, Mexico.

with Kenya and Tanzania producing purple (Umba River region) and golden green crystals, Mozambique green apatites, and Namibia and South Africa blue–green stones. Very fine and sometimes large blue, green, or blue–green apatites, many sold for use in jewelry, have been found in Madagascar. Light blue crystals up to 10 cm are also known from Australia. Russia has significant deposits of yellow or yellow–green (Kola Peninsula) and blue, sometimes chatoyant (Transbaikalia) apatite. Tajikistan (Pamir Mts.) has produced pink, and Kazakhstan yellow or colorless, stones. Other apatite occurrences are known from Canada (Ontario; Quebec – crystals up to 70 cm), Italy (colorless), Switzerland, Austria, Spain (yellow–green), Portugal, Finland, Sweden, Germany. Gems are often over 100 ct., the largest yellow–green cut apatite from Kenya weighing 147 ct.

Processing: faceted cuts, cabochons

Similar minerals: aquamarine, goshenite, heliodor, amethyst, smoky quartz

Imitations: synthetic apatite

Identification: hardness, specific gravity, optical methods

Care: Protect apatite from sudden temperature changes, which may cause color to change or fade, abrasion, and acids. Clean in soap and water only; do not use ultrasonic or steam cleaning.

Rough apatites; largest, 25 mm, Brazil.

Smithsonite

$ZnCO_3$

After J. Smithson

History: Formally described in 1832, smithsonite is important as a gemstone only to collectors.

Host rocks: supergene zones of ore deposits

Occurrences: Found in large quantities in Vietnam, smithsonite also occurs in Kazakhstan, Turkey, and Australia. Intense green, pink, white, and gray crusts up to 8 cm thick are known from Namibia (Tsumeb), with crystals coming from Zambia, Kenya, and Algeria. Nice botryoidal crusts have been found in Arkansas (yellow), New Mexico (Kelly Mine – apple green, blue–green), Colorado (green–blue), Montana, California. Mexican smithsonite also occurs in a variety of colors. Many deposits are known from Russia (Ural Mts.), Greece, Italy, the United Kingdom, and Spain.

Processing: faceted cuts, cabochons, small glyptics

Similar minerals: jadeite, chalcedony,

Color: white, gray, yellow, green–blue, blue, also red, orange–red, pink; rarely colorless • **Diaphaneity:** rarely transparent, translucent • **Luster:** glassy, pearly, dull • **Fracture:** uneven, splintery • **Cleavage:** perfect • **Hardness:** 4–4.5, brittle • **Streak:** white • **Specific gravity:** 4.3–4.4 • **Refractive index:** N_e–1.621, N_o–1.848–1.849 • **Birefringence:** 0.227 • **Dispersion:** 0.037 • **Pleochroism:** none • **Luminescence:** sometimes white, blue–white, green–white, pink, brown • **Chemistry:** color caused by trace amounts of Cd (yellow), Co (pink), Cu and Fe (blue) • **Special features:** none • **Treatment:** not known

chrysoprase, hemimorphite, turquoise

Imitations: glass

Identification: hardness, specific gravity, optical methods

Care: Protect smithsonite from sudden shocks, sudden temperature changes, abrasion, and HCl. Clean in soap and water only; do not use ultrasonic or steam cleaning.

Smithsonite, 174 mm wide, Kelly Mine, New Mexico.

Variscite

$AlPO_4 \cdot 2H_2O$

After Variscia, Latin name
for Vogtland, Germany

History: Formally described in 1837, variscite is used as a gemstone in only a few places in the world.

Host rocks: oxidation zones

Occurrences: Variscite occurs in the United States (Arizona, Utah, Nevada), Bolivia (Huanuni, Cerro Posocani), Brazil, and Australia. It has also been found in Germany, Austria, and Spain.

Processing: cabochons, small glyptics, table cuts

Similar minerals: turquoise, jadeite, chrysoprase

Variscite, 153 mm wide, Fairfield, Utah.

4

Color: green, blue–green, yellow, colorless • **Diaphaneity:** transparent, opaque • **Luster:** glassy, greasy, dull • **Fracture:** conchoidal • **Cleavage:** good • **Hardness:** 2.2–2.57 • **Refractive index:** N_p–1.550–1.563, N_m–1.565–1.588, N_g–1.570–1.594 • **Birefringence:** 0.031 • **Dispersion:** none • **Pleochroism:** none • **Luminescence:** none • **Chemistry:** color caused by trace amounts of Cr, Fe • **Special features:** none • **Treatment:** not known

Imitations: not known

Identification: hardness, specific gravity, optical methods

Care: Protect variscite from sudden shocks, sudden temperature changes, abrasion, and acids. Clean in soap and water only; do not use ultrasonic or steam cleaning.

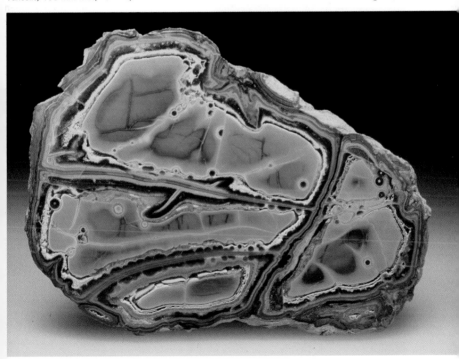

Fluorite

CaF$_2$

From New Latin *fluor* – "flow" for use as flux

History: Fluorite was known to the ancient Greeks and Romans, who used it to make vases and other vessels. The "**Blue John**" variety was very popular in 19th–century England.
Astrology: birthstone for Pisces
Chakra: crown

Color: highly variable; mostly green, blue–green, purple to purple–red, yellow, wine red, brown, orange, white, colorless; less often pink, blue, black; some fluorites are banded with different colors • **Diaphaneity:** transparent, semitransparent • **Luster:** glassy • **Fracture:** uneven • **Cleavage:** perfect • **Hardness:** 4, brittle • **Streak:** white • **Specific gravity:** 3.0–3.25 • **Refractive index:** N–1.432–1.434 • **Birefringence:** none • **Dispersion:** 0.007 • **Pleochroism:** none • **Luminescence:** blue, purple, yellow, white, green, red; phosphoresces when heated (thermoluminescence) • **Chemistry:** trace amounts of Cl, REE, other elements • **Special features:** alexandrite effect • **Treatment:** irradiation, heating, proofing

Multicolored step cut fluorite, 70 ct., Chile.

Fluorite on quartz; largest crystal, 30 mm, Chamonix, France.

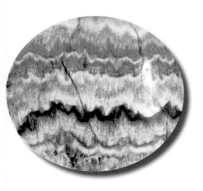

Banded fluorite variety ("Blue John"), Cumberland, United Kingdom.

and Korea (492 and 354 ct.), a red English gem (118 ct.), and yellow and purple gems from Illinois (351 and 111.2 ct.). Probably the largest fluorite gem, a blue stone weighing 3,965.35 ct. in the same collection, was cut by Art Grant.

Processing: faceted cuts, cabochons, small to large glyptics, table cuts

Similar minerals: barite, apatite, amethyst

Imitations: glass

Identification: hardness, specific gravity, optical methods

Care: Protect fluorite from sudden shocks, sudden temperature changes, abrasion, and H_2SO_4. Clean in soap and water only; do not use ultrasonic or steam cleaning.

Healing effects: calms emotions; strengthens heart; discharge stone in soft water, then recharge briefly in sunlight

Host rocks: pegmatites, hydrothermal deposits

Occurrences: Very important deposits of often fine–banded, multicolored fluorite crystals are located in China. Fluorite has also been found in Mongolia, Korea, Pakistan (fine pink crystals), and Australia. Many fine occurrences in the United States include New Mexico, Utah (light green crystals), Colorado, Kentucky, New Hampshire (light green crystals), Texas (large crystals of different colors), Tennessee (blue–green crystals), New York, and Illinois (yellow and purple crystals). Fluorite is known from Canada, Mexico (Zacatecas – emerald green crystals; Guanajuato – red crystals), Peru (pink), Argentina, Colombia, Namibia (green crystals), and South Africa. It also occurs in Russia, Kazakhstan, and Tajikistan. Famous fluorites have been found in the United Kingdom (Cumberland), Spain, Germany, the Czech Republic, Italy, Norway, France, Switzerland, and Romania. Fluorite has been used for both faceting and lapidary objects. The Smithsonian Institution in Washington, D.C., has a suite of faceted, different–colored fluorite gems, including pink faceted gems from Pakistan (248.8 ct.)

Fluorite, 72 mm high, Pine Canyon deposit, Grant Co., New Mexico.

Rhodochrosite

$MnCO_3$

From Greek *rhodon* +
chros = "rose–colored"

History: Argentina has the longest tradition of using rhodochrosite to make lapidary objects. Called the "Rose of Incas," it was mined there by the Indians in the 13th century.

Astrology: birthstone for Aries

Chakra: heart

Healing effects: improves thinking; discharge stone in soft water, then recharge briefly in sunlight

Host rocks: hydrothermal deposits, metamorphic and sedimentary rocks

Color: pink, red, brown–red, gray, often banded • **Diaphaneity:** transparent, translucent • **Luster:** glassy, pearly • **Fracture:** conchoidal • **Cleavage:** perfect • **Hardness:** 3.5–4, brittle • **Streak:** white • **Specific gravity:** 3.4–4, brittle • **Refractive index:** N_e–1.578–1.695, N_o–1.786–1.840 • **Birefringence:** 0.201–0.220 • **Dispersion:** none • **Pleochroism:** sometimes weak (intensely colored stones) • **Luminescence:** sometimes light pink to dark red • **Chemistry:** trace amounts of Ca, Fe • **Special features:** none • **Treatment:** not known

Rhodochrosite, 113 mm high, Sweet Home Mine, Alma, Colorado.

Occurrences: Gemmy rhodochrosite comes chiefly from the Americas; the best deposits are in Colorado (Sweet Home Mine – material suitable for faceting gems over 60 ct.) and Montana. Argentina is at present the main producer, with deposits in San Luis and Catamarca Provinces (Las Capillitas). Nice ruby red crystals have been found in Mexico and Peru. Superb deep red crystals up to 7 cm from South Africa (N'Chwaning Mine, Kuruman) have yielded cut stones up to 5 ct. Fine rhodochrosites are also known from Russia (Transbaikalia, Ural Mts.) and Romania, where they usually form fine–banded botryoidal aggregates (Cavnic, Baia Sprie), but sometimes crystals (Sacarimb). Less important occurrences are in India, Afghanistan, Australia. Rhodochrosites have also been found in Germany, the Czech Republic, Slovakia, France, Spain, Serbia, and Bulgaria. Lapidary objects made of rhodochrosite are preserved in museums all over the world. While faceted gems over 20 ct. are rare, the Smithsonian Institution in Washington, D.C., has a red cut stone weighing 59.65 ct.

Processing: faceted cuts, cabochons, table cuts, small to medium glyptics

Slice of rhodochrosite stalactite, 84 mm wide, Catamarca, Argentina.

Similar minerals: dolomite, rose quartz, rhodonite
Imitations: not known

Identification: hardness, specific gravity, optical methods; reacts with HCl
Care: Protect rhodochrosite from sudden shocks, sudden temperature changes, heat or flame, abrasion, and HCl. Clean in soap and water only; do not use ultrasonic or steam cleaning.

Rhodochrosite polished section, Cavnic, Romania.

Rhodochrosite polished section, Catamarca, Argentina.

Malachite

$Cu_2(CO_3)(OH)_2$

From Greek *malache*
– "mallow," hence "leaf green"

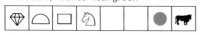

History: Cameos, amulets, and lapidary objects were made of malachite in ancient Egypt, Greece, and Rome. Crushed stones were used as a pigment in painting and makeup. Malachite was believed to protect children from magic and witchcraft, to help them grow, and to soothe their aches and pains.

Astrology: birthstone for Taurus

Chakra: heart

Healing effects: sharpens eyesight; used to treat ailments of pancreas, spleen, stomach (especially colic), also emotional problems, insomnia, headaches; discharge stone in lukewarm water, then recharge briefly in sunlight

Host rocks: oxidation zones of copper deposits

Occurrences: Extensive malachite deposits have been found in China, India, Australia, and the United States (Arizona, Nevada, Colorado, Utah). Gemmy malachites are known from Chile, Mexico, and Cuba; nice malachite crusts, similar to those in the Democratic Republic of the Congo (Zaire), occur in Nicaragua. The most important deposits – and the world's best

Color: green, dark green, black–green, light green; rarely blue–green to emerald green; often banded • **Diaphaneity:** opaque, rarely translucent • **Luster:** glassy, silky, dull, adamantine (crystals) • **Fracture:** conchoidal, splintery • **Cleavage:** perfect • **Hardness:** 3.5–4.5, brittle • **Streak:** light green • **Specific gravity:** 4.5 • **Refractive index:** N_p–1.655, N_m–1.875, N_g–1.909 • **Birefringence:** 0.254 • **Dispersion:** none • **Pleochroism:** distinct – colorless, yellow–green, dark green • **Luminescence:** none • **Chemistry:** color caused by Cu • **Special features:** none • **Treatment:** proofing with paraffin or epoxy

Lapidary objects and polished section of malachite (70 mm wide), Democratic Republic of Congo (Zaire).

Box made of malachite, combined with jasper. Russian work from beginning of 20th century.

Malachite stalactites, Democratic Republic of Congo (Zaire).

malachite – have long been mined in Africa's Copperbelt region, from Shaba Province in the Democratic Republic of the Congo (Zaire) to Zambia, with nice malachite crystals coming from Namibia (Tsumeb), Morocco, Zimbabwe, and Angola. Very important deposits, mined since 1709 (Gumeshevsk deposit), occur in Russia (vicinity of Nizhni Tagil in Ural Mts.), where the malachite–bearing zone reaches a depth of 130 m and where blocks weighing several tons (up to 8 x 1 m) have been found. Nice malachite occurs in Kazakhstan, as well. Less important occurrences are in Germany, Slovakia, Hungary, Romania, the United Kingdom, and France. Lapidary malachite objects are popular items in museum displays. The Georgievskii halls of St. Petersburg's Winter Palace are among the best examples of decorative malachite. A large collection of Russian malachite jewelry is on display at Versailles.

Processing: cabochons, table cuts, small to large glyptics, facing, faceted cuts (rare)

Similar minerals: pseudomalachite

Imitations: glass

Identification: hardness, specific gravity

Care: Protect malachite from sudden shocks, sudden temperature changes, abrasion, and acids. Clean in soap and water only; do not use ultrasonic or steam cleaning.

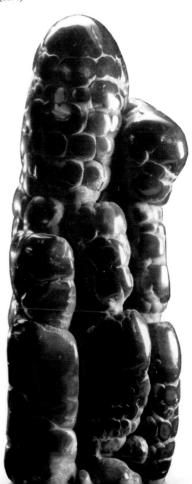

Aragonite

$CaCO_3$

After (Molina de)
Aragon, Spain

History: Variously banded and easily workable, massive aragonite has long been used to make bowls, sculptures, and facings.

Host rocks: low–temperature veins in sedimentary and metamorphic rocks

Occurrences: Massive aragonite has been found in many deposits in South Dakota, New Mexico, Iowa, Indiana, Wyoming, and Montana (red). It also occurs in Canada, Mexico (green), Chile (blue), Peru, Argentina, as well as in Namibia, Madagascar, Algeria, and Morocco (red). Aragonite is known from Turkmenistan, Kyrgystan (blue), Germany, Austria, Slovakia, Spain,

Lapidary aragonite objects, Pakistan.

Color: colorless, white, yellow, brown–green, gray–white, pink, light purple, bluish, red, orange • **Diaphaneity:** transparent to translucent, opaque • **Luster:** glassy to silky • **Fracture:** conchoidal • **Cleavage:** good to poor • **Hardness:** 3.5–4, brittle • **Streak:** white • **Specific gravity:** 2.93–2.95 • **Refractive index:** N_p–1.530, N_m–1.681, N_g–1.685 • **Birefringence:** 0.155 • **Dispersion:** weak • **Pleochroism:** none • **Luminescence:** white, yellow, creamy, orange, green • **Chemistry:** trace amounts of Fe, Pb, Sr, Zn • **Special features:** none • **Treatment:** not known

Cut aragonite, 91.69 ct., Hořenec near Bílina, Czech Republic.

Greece (blue), with fine green stones coming from Pakistan. Hořenec near Bílina (Czech Republic), where J. W. Goethe collected, is the only locality in the world producing gem rough suitable for faceting. Colorless, yellow to greenish cut gems rarely exceed 100 ct.

Processing: faceted cuts, cabochons, small to medium glyptics, table cuts

Similar minerals: calcite

Imitations: not known

Identification: specific gravity, hardness

Care: Protect aragonite from sudden shocks, sudden temperature changes, abrasion, and acids. Clean in soap and water only; do not use ultrasonic or steam cleaning.

Calcite

CaCO₃

$CaCO_3$

After chemical composition

History: Onyx was especially popular in ancient Egypt, Assyria, Babylonia, and Rome, where mosaics, sculptures, and whole interiors of palaces were made of it. Because of calcite's perfect cleavage, faceted gems are fairly rare.

Host rocks: igneous, metamorphic, and sedimentary rocks, hydrothermal deposits, weathering zones, oxidation zones, thermal springs

Chakra: heart

Healing effects: strengthens heart, nervous system

Occurrences: Onyx varieties are known from Indonesia, Egypt (multicolored), Afghanistan, Pakistan, Russia, Turkmenistan, Uzbekistan, and Germany. "**Utah onyx**" is known from the United States. Onyx also comes from Mexico, Argentina, Australia, New Zealand, Algeria, and Morocco; blue stones come from Namibia, and light yellow stones from Kenya. Gem roughs for faceting come mainly from the Tunguska River basin in Russia, where clear yellow crystals reach up to several kilograms. Pink–purple sphaerocobaltites from the

Cut calcite with strong birefringence, 85 ct., Tunguska, Russia.

Color: colorless, white, yellow, brown, red, blue, green, black; often banded (*onyx*) • **Diaphaneity:** transparent to translucent, opaque • **Luster:** glassy, pearly on cleavage planes • **Fracture:** conchoidal • **Cleavage:** perfect • **Hardness:** 3, brittle • **Streak:** white • **Specific gravity:** 2.71–2.94 • **Refractive index:** N_e– 1.486–1.550, N_o–1.658–1.740 • **Birefringence:** 0.172–0.190 • **Dispersion:** distinct • **Pleochroism:** none • **Luminescence:** white, yellow, blue, red, orange, green • **Chemistry:** traces of Mn, Pb, Sr, Co (**sphaerocobaltite**) • **Special features:** very strong birefringence (*Iceland spar*), chatoyancy (fibrous varieties) • **Treatment:** grainy varieties (*marble*) are proofed, dyed, heated, or irradiated

Democratic Republic of the Congo (Zaire) are very popular, but gems rarely exceed 10 ct. The Harvard University has a cut stone from Canada, weighing 1,260 ct.

Processing: cabochons, glyptics, table cuts, faceted cuts (rare)

Similar minerals: aragonite

Identification: hardness, cleavage; reacts with acids

Care: Protect calcite from sudden shocks, sudden temperature changes, abrasion, acids, and detergents. Clean in soap and water; do not use ultrasonic or steam cleaning.

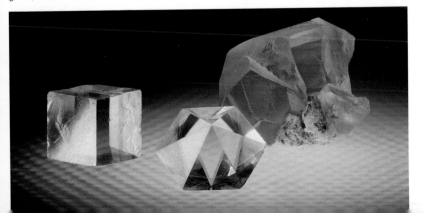

Cuprite

Cu₂O

Cu_2O

From Latin *cuprum*
– "copper"

History: Formally described in 1845, cuprite is only important as a gemstone to collectors.
Host rocks: oxidation zone of copper deposits
Occurrences: Very important deposits are known from Arizona (Bisbee – crystals up to 3 cm) and New Mexico, also from Chile, Peru, and Australia. Perhaps the best–known crystals come from Namibia (Tsumeb, Onganja); those from Onganja (up to 5–10 cm) are translucent and of gem quality. Nice crystals have also been found in Hungary (Rudabánya). The American Museum of Natural History in New York has a cut stone from Namibia weighing 172 ct. The Smithsonian Institution in Washington, D.C., has a cut stone weighing 203.75 ct; another weighing 299.5 ct. is in a private collection. Rare faceted stones up to 300 ct. have been cut, but larger gem roughs usually lack translucency. Very attractive cabochons are cut out of massive cuprite, associated

Color: brown–red, red–black, crimson red, red, black • **Diaphaneity:** transparent to translucent, opaque • **Luster:** adamantine, submetallic to dull • **Fracture:** conchoidal to uneven • **Cleavage:** poor • **Hardness:** 3.5–4, brittle • **Streak:** brown–red • **Specific gravity:** 6.15 • **Refractive index:** N–2.848 • **Birefringence:** none • **Dispersion:** none • **Pleochroism:** none • **Luminescence:** none • **Chemistry:** color caused by Cu • **Special features:** none • **Treatment:** not known

with green and blue secondary copper minerals from various localities.
Processing: faceted cuts, cabochons
Similar minerals: cinnabar, pyrargyrite, proustite
Identification: hardness, specific gravity
Care: Protect cuprite from heat or flame and abrasion. Surface oxidation is typical, resulting in a thin opaque layer. Clean in soap and water only.

Cuprite crystal, 18 mm wide, Mashamba West, Democratic Republic of Congo (Zaire).

Sphalerite

ZnS

From Greek *sphaleros* – "deceitful" because it was often mistaken for galena

Color: light to dark brown, yellow, green, black, orange; rarely colorless • **Diaphaneity:** transparent (*cleiophane*) to opaque (*marmatite*) • **Luster:** silky to adamantine • **Fracture:** conchoidal • Cleavage: perfect • **Hardness:** 3.5–4, brittle • **Streak:** light brown • **Specific gravity:** 3.9–4.1 • **Refractive index:** N–2.37–2.43 • **Birefringence:** none • **Dispersion:** 0.156 • **Pleochroism:** none • **Chemistry:** trace amounts of Cd, Fe, In • **Special features:** none • **Treatment:** not known

History: Formally described in 1847, sphalerite is popular as a gemstone, but only among collectors.

Host rocks: igneous rocks, hydrothermal deposits, sedimentary rocks

Occurrences: Sphalerite is known from many deposits in Nevada, Montana, Utah, Tennessee, Ohio (Tiffin – ruby red crystals), also Mexico, the Democratic Republic of the Congo (Zaire), Germany, the Czech Republic, Slovakia (yellow crystals), Switzerland, Poland, Serbia (Trepca), and Romania. The best gem rough for cutting comes from Spain (Picos de Europa – yellow to red crystals), but similar material has recently come to the market from Kazakhstan (Dzhezkazgan) and Bulgaria (Madan).

Processing: faceted cuts, cabochons, table cuts

Similar minerals: cassiterite, spessartine

Imitations: synthetic sphalerite

Identification: hardness, specific gravity, optical methods

Care: Protect from shocks, temperature changes, and abrasion. Clean in soap and water; do not use ultrasonic or steam.

Different–colored sphalerites; largest cut stone, 25 ct., Dzhezkazgan, Kazakhstan.

Polished section of sphalerite, associated with galena, Olkusz, Poland.

Azurite

Cu₃(CO₃)₂(OH)₂

From Persian *lazhuward*
– "sky blue, azure"

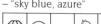

History: Although formally described in 1805 and often used as a pigment, azurite is only rarely used as a gemstone.
Astrology: birthstone for Pisces
Chakra: forehead
Healing effects: strengthens memory; speeds healing of injuries; discharge stone in lukewarm water, then recharge briefly in sunlight
Host rocks: oxidation zones of copper deposits
Occurrences: Very fine azurites have been found in Arizona (azurite–malachite concretions), also in Utah and New Mexico. Numerous occurrences are in Chile, Australia, the Democratic Republic of the Congo (Zaire; azurite–malachite concretions from Shaba Province). Fine crystals are known from Morocco, Kenya, and Namibia (crystals up to 20 cm). Azurite also occurs in Russia (Ural Mts.), China, Germany, Hungary, Slovakia, France, Greece, and Romania. Faceted stones do not exceed a few carats; larger gem roughs are opaque.
Processing: cabochons, small carvings, faceted cuts (rare)
Similar minerals: vivianite, lazurite, hauyne
Imitations: glass

Color: light to dark azure blue, blue–purple • **Diaphaneity:** translucent, opaque • **Luster:** dull, glassy (crystals) • **Fracture:** conchoidal • **Cleavage:** perfect • **Hardness:** 3.5–4, brittle • **Streak:** light blue • **Specific gravity:** 3.77 • **Refractive index:** N_p–1.730, N_m–1.758, N_g–1.838 • **Birefringence:** 0.110 • **Dispersion:** visible • **Pleochroism:** distinct (blue varieties) • **Luminescence:** none • **Chemistry:** color caused by Cu • **Special features:** none • **Treatment:** proofing with paraffin or epoxy

Azurite–malachite, *Arizona.*

Identification: hardness, specific gravity
Care: Treat like turquoise.

Azurite, 11 mm wide, Morenci, Arizona.

Chrysocolla

$(Cu^{2+},Al)_2H_2Si_2O_5(OH)_4 \cdot nH_2O$

From Greek *chrysos* + *kolla* = "gold glue" for its use as flux in gold soldering

◈	⌒	▢	🐎			●	🏃

History: First mentioned by Theophrastos (372–287 B.C.).
Astrology: birthstone for Gemini
Chakra: heart
Healing effects: helps prevent ulcers; quiets spasms; discharge stone in lukewarm water, then recharge briefly in sunlight
Host rocks: oxidation zone of copper deposits
Occurrences: Although very common, chrysocolla is seldom of gem quality. Important occurrences are in the United States (Nevada, New Mexico, Arizona, Idaho, and California), Mexico, Chile, Peru and Canada. Nice chrysocolla comes from Israel (Eilat), South Africa, the Democratic Republic of the Congo (Zaire), Zimbabwe, Russia (Ural Mts.), Kazakhstan, and Moldavia.
Processing: cabochons, small carvings, table cuts, faceted cuts (rare)
Similar minerals: shattuckite, turquoise
Identification: hardness, specific gravity
Care: Protect from sudden temperature changes, abrasion, and acids. Clean in soap and water only.

Polished section of chrysocolla with native copper, Arizona.

Color: green–blue to blue; also emerald green, turquoise blue • **Diaphaneity:** translucent, opaque • **Luster:** glassy, greasy, dull • **Fracture:** uneven to conchoidal • **Cleavage:** none • **Hardness:** 2–4 (up to 6 when intergrown with quartz) • **Streak:** light green • **Specific gravity:** 2.0–2.45 • **Refractive index:** N_p–1.575–1.585, N_m–1.587, N_g–1.598–1.635 • **Birefringence:** 0.023–0.040 • **Dispersion:** none • **Pleochroism:** weak • **Luminescence:** none • **Chemistry:** trace amounts of Al, Fe • **Special features:** common quartz intergrowths • **Treatment:** proofing with paraffin or epoxy

4

Chrysocolla, 22 mm wide, Gila Co., Arizona.

Amber

From Arabic *anbar* – "ambergris," for which it was first mistaken

History: Amber amulets and trading beads have been found in Paleolithic graves. Highly prized by the ancient Greeks, amber was believed to protect its owner from rheumatism and, as a powder mixed with oil or water, to heal a wide variety of ills.
Astrology: birthstone for Leo
Chakra: navel
Healing effects: used to treat ailments of eyes, ears, teeth, also lungs, stomach, urinary bladder; discharge stone in lukewarm water, then recharge briefly in sunlight|
Source: trees (amber is fossilized resin, formed chiefly from sap of prehistoric pine trees)
Occurrences: Amber comes from all over the world. The best–known deposits are concentrated in the "Amber Province" on the Baltic Sea, an area 2,000 km (1,250 mi) long and 500 km (300 mi) wide, where amber has been mined for many centuries, and where masses up to 10 kg have been recovered. Amber occurs in Germany, Denmark, Poland, Lithuania, Latvia, Estonia, Russia, Ukraine, Armenia, and Azerbaijan. Cretaceous–age amber

Color: honey yellow, orange, yellow–white, hyacinth red; rarely blue, greenish, black • **Diaphaneity:** transparent to translucent, opaque • **Luster:** greasy, dull • **Fracture:** conchoidal • **Cleavage:** none • **Hardness:** 2–2.5 • **Streak:** white • **Specific gravity:** 1.05–1.096 • **Refractive index:** N–1.537–1.545 • **Birefringence:** none • **Dispersion:** none • **Pleochroism:** none • **Luminescence:** bluish, yellow • **Chemistry:** color caused by free electrons in organic molecules; bluish color due to strong fluorescence • **Special features:** generates static electricity when rubbed • **Treatment:** heating in oil, hot pressing

has been found on the Arabian Peninsula. Other localities are in Syria, Lebanon, Burma (**birmite** – wine yellow, red; rarely green and blue), China (**retinite**), Japan, Thailand, Vietnam, and Malaysia. It is also known from Canada (**cedarite**), Maryland, Washington, Alaska ("arctic" amber), Mexico, the Dominican Republic (important producer of blue amber), Argentina (Patagonia – **ambrite**), Greenland (**schraufite**), New Zealand (**kauri**), the Fiji and Vanuatu Islands. African amber comes from South Africa, Guinea,

Detail of insect trapped in amber 25 mm wide, Colombia.

Amber mass, 45 mm wide, Colombia. Beads are made of Baltic amber from Poland.

Zimbabwe, Sierra Leone, Ghana, Angola, the Democratic Republic of the Congo (Zaire), Nigeria, Madagascar. Less common amber varieties have been found in Hungary (*ajkaite*), Romania (*rumenite*), the Czech Republic (*valchovite, neudorfite*), Spain (red *retitite*), Poland (*kopalite*), the United Kingdom, and Italy (*simetite* from Sicily). Amber from the resin of the tree *Dammara orientalis* has recently been formed in Tanzania, Mozambique, and Madagascar, and is also forming in Malaysia and on many Pacific islands. Of the many historical works in amber, the most famous is the Amber Chamber, made in Prussia in 1701–1709 and given to the Russian czar Peter I in 1716. Transported to Czarskoye selo in 1755, the Amber Chamber was moved to Königsberg (now Kaliningrad) during World War II. Since then, its fate remains unknown.

Processing: cabochons, beads, lapidary objects, faceted cuts (rare)

Similar minerals: none

Imitations: bakelite, celluloid, epoxy, pressed amber (ambroid), copal

Identification: specific gravity, optical methods

Care: Protect amber from heat or flame, abrasion, acids, and alcohols, also from perspiration and direct sunlight, which cause stones to age and lose their luster. Clean in soap and water; do not use steam cleaning.

Agalmatolite

(pyrophyllite variety)

$Al_2Si_4O_{10}(OH)_2$

From Greek *agalma* + *lithos*
= "figure stone" for earliest use

History: Known as a gemstone to the ancient Egyptians, Greeks, and Chinese, agalmatolite is still popular in China today.

Host rocks: hydrothermal deposits, metamorphic rocks

Occurrences: One of the largest deposits is in Tibet, where agalmatolite (sometimes in huge blocks) is mined to this day. Also known from Japan, South Korea, and Mongolia, it has been found in the United States (California, Georgia), Brazil, South Africa, Russia, Uzbekistan, Ukraine, Germany, Finland, England, and Scotland.

Processing: cabochons, carvings, lapidary objects, engravings

Color: white, gray, yellow, greenish, gray–green, red–brown • **Diaphaneity:** translucent • **Luster:** pearly to greasy, dull • **Fracture:** uneven, splintery • **Cleavage:** perfect • **Hardness:** 1–2 • **Streak:** white • **Specific gravity:** 2.65–2.90 • **Refractive index:** N_p–1.534–1.556, N_m–1.586–1.589, N_g–1.596–1.601 • **Birefringence:** 0.050 • **Dispersion:** weak • **Pleochroism:** weak • **Luminescence:** very weak brown–white, white, yellow, orange • **Chemistry:** rich green color caused by trace amounts of Cr • **Special features:** feels greasy • **Treatment:** not known

Similar minerals: talc
Imitations: talc
Identification: hardness
Care: Protect from abrasion. Clean in distilled water; do not use steam cleaning.

Lapidary objects made of agalmatolite; oval box is 60 mm wide, India.

Ulexite

$NaCaB_5O_6(OH)_6 \cdot 5H_2O$

After G. L. Ulex

History: Described in 1850, ulexite is used as a gemstone only locally and on a small scale. Because its parallel fibers make it a good optical conductor, it is also called "**TV stone**."

Host rocks: sedimentary rocks

Occurrences: While found mainly in California, where its fibrous aggregates reach 10 cm in length, ulexite also occurs in Nevada, Oregon, and Texas. Other localities are in Canada, Peru (near Arequipi), Argentina (Tres Mares), Chile, Kazakhstan (Inder Lake), Turkey (Emet region), Italy.

Color: colorless, white • **Diaphaneity:** transparent to translucent • **Luster:** glassy, silky • **Fracture:** uneven, splintery • **Cleavage:** perfect, good • **Hardness:** 1–2.5, brittle • **Streak:** white • **Specific gravity:** 1.65–1.95 • **Refractive index:** N_p–1.496, N_m–1.505, N_g–1.519 • **Birefringence:** 0.023 • **Dispersion:** none • **Pleochroism:** none • **Luminescence:** blue, green • **Special features:** chatoyancy • **Treatment:** not known

Processing: cabochons, plates, faceted cuts (rare)

Similar minerals: colemanite, selenite

Imitations: none

Identification: hardness, specific gravity, optical methods

Care: Protect ulexite from heat or flame, abrasion, soaps, and detergents. Clean in cold water only; do not use steam cleaning.

Ulexite, 50 mm wide, California.

Gypsum

$CaSO_4 \cdot 2H_2O$

From Greek *gypsos*
– "chalk, cement, gypsum"

Color: colorless, white, gray, blue, yellow, brown, pinkish • **Diaphaneity:** transparent to translucent • **Luster:** glassy, pearly on cleavage planes • **Fracture:** conchoidal, splintery • **Cleavage:** perfect, good • **Hardness:** 2 • **Streak:** white • **Specific gravity:** 2.3–2.33 • **Refractive index:** N_p–1.521, N_m–1.523, N_g–1.531 • **Birefringence:** 0.010 • **Dispersion:** 0.033 • **Pleochroism:** none • **Luminescence:** sometimes brown, yellow, green • **Special features:** chatoyancy • **Treatment:** dyeing, proofing

History: Alabaster sculptures are known from ancient Egypt.

Host rocks: sedimentary rocks, hydrothermal deposits

Occurrences: Dense, fine–grained gypsum is called *alabaster*; fibrous chatoyant gypsum is called *selenite* in Europe, and *satin spar* in the United States, where name selenite generally describes transparent crystals of gypsum. A very important raw material, gypsum is also used as a gemstone. Probably the best gypsum crystals ever found came from Mexico (Naica – clear crystals up to 1.3 m long). It also occurs in Kansas, Colorado, New Mexico, and Chile. Other localities are in Canada (Winnipeg), Russia, Kazakhstan, Morocco, Tunisia, and Algeria ("Sahara roses"). Nice crystals have been found in Germany (Eis-

Lapidary objects made of fibrous variety of gypsum (satin spar). Sculpture, 75 mm high, is contemporary Russian work.

Druse of gypsum crystals, 12 mm wide, Mexico.

Polished section of fine-grained gypsum, Rothleben, Germany.

leben), France, Italy, Romania (Baia Sprie), Austria, Poland. Transparent to translucent, white and orange, pinkish in spots, selenites are known from Russia (Ural Mts. near Kungur).
Processing: cabochons, lapidary objects, faceted cuts
Similar minerals: anhydrite, celestine
Identification: hardness

Pearl

$CaCO_3$

From Vulgar Latin *pernula*, dim. of *perna* – "sea mussel," one of earliest sources

3

History: Prized by the ancient Egyptians, pearl has been known for over 6,000 years. Well-preserved pearls were found in the excavations in Mexico (2500 B.C) and in the ruins of Pompeii (79 B.C.), even though surface layers generally peel off after 100–150 years. A symbol of power, wisdom, and happiness to the Romans, and believed to bring sweet dreams to women, pearl was used as a talisman by the Indians and in concoctions to strengthen masculinity by the Mongolians.

Astrology: birthstone for Gemini
Chakra: throat
Healing effects: used to treat ailments of nose, throat, lungs; discharge stone in cold water, then recharge briefly in sunlight
Source: saltwater and freshwater mollusks, most notably oysters
Occurrences: Pearl–producing lamellibranchs are hunted in warm tropical seas, but most pearls come from hatcheries. Natural pearls come from Sri Lanka,

Color: white with different–colored hues (best are pink and bluish); also silver, golden (***Panama pearls***), green, black; sometimes iridescent colors • **Diaphaneity:** translucent, transparent • **Luster:** pearly, dull • **Fracture:** uneven • **Cleavage:** none • **Hardness:** 2.5–4.5 • **Streak:** white • **Specific gravity:** 2.60–2.78 (lamellibranch pearls), 2.85 (conch pearls) • **Refractive index:** N $-1.52-1.66$ (black pearls $-1.53-1.69$) • **Birefringence:** 0.126 • **Dispersion:** none • **Pleochroism:** none • **Luminescence:** bluish, yellowish, pinkish • **Chemistry:** 82–86% aragonite ($CaCO_3$), 10–14% conchioline (organic substance), 2% water • **Special features:** pearly luster • **Treatment:** dyeing, irradiation, heating

Detail of petrified pearl layer of Mesozoic ammonite ("ammolite").

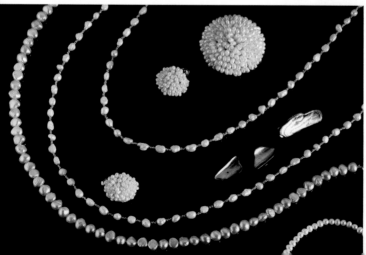

Jewelry made of cultivated pearls.

southern India (Manara Bay), the Arabian Sea (Saudi Arabia, Iran, Oman), and the Red Sea (known for over 2,500 years). They also occur near Tahiti, Japan, Mexico, Panama, and California. Less important are freshwater pearls from the Mississippi River basin and historical freshwater European pearls from Germany and the Czech Republic. They are also known from Russia (Siberia). Freshwater pearls from China have recently appeared on the market.

Processing: used in natural shape, drilled and cut

Similar minerals: none

Imitations: glass, mother–of–pearl

Identification: chemical, other special tests, X–rays

Care: Protect pearls from heat or flame, abrasion, acids, perspiration, and cosmetics. Clean in soap and lukewarm water; do not use ultrasonic or steam cleaning.

Different colors and shapes of pearls; black pearl is 12 mm.

Gold ring with different colored pearls, by Karel Valter, Geneva.

Coral

CaCO₃

From Greek *korallion*
– "red coral"

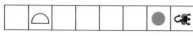

History: Found in archaeological sites dating back to 10,000 B.C., coral was popular in ancient Egypt and known to the Celtic tribes. The name itself may be of Celtic origin.
Astrology: birthstone for Scorpio
Chakra: base
Healing effects: sharpens mental acuity; used to treat ailments of urinary system, also eyes; discharge stone in cold water, then recharge briefly in sunlight
Source: sea polyps, which form colonies to a depth of 3,200 m (10,500 ft; coral is the polyps' outer skeleton, composed chiefly of calcite)

Color: red (*oxblood*, *morro*), pink (*momo coral* from Taiwan – salmon pink); rarely white, bluish, black, pink–white ("*spotted coral*" from a depth of 200 m or 650 ft), silvery–pearly (highly valued "*angel coral*") • **Diaphaneity:** opaque • **Luster:** dull to glassy • **Fracture:** splintery, hackly • **Cleavage:** none • **Hardness:** 3.5–4 • **Streak:** white • **Specific gravity:** 2.6–2.7 (black ones 1.34–1.36) • **Refractive index:** N–1.486–1.658 • **Birefringence:** 0.160–0.172 • **Dispersion:** none • **Pleochroism:** none • **Luminescence:** light purple to dark purple • **Chemistry:** calcite with traces of CaSO₃, NA₂SO₃, K₂SO₃, MgCl₂, I • **Special features:** none • **Treatment:** proofing, heating, dyeing

Gold brooch with corals, diamonds, and moldavite, by Gilbert Albert, Geneva.

Occurrences: About 6,000 species of coral polyps are now known. They form sometimes immense reefs (Great Barrier Reef in Australia is over 2,300 km or 1,400 mi long). Coral occurs in warm and clean seas the world over. Historically, coral is known from the Mediterranean (Tunisia, Algeria, Italy, Corsica, Sardinia and Sicily), where red and orange–red coral is most common. It is also found in the Bay of Biscay (France and Spain). White coral is known from the Sea of Japan, while salmon red comes from Taiwan. Pink coral is known from Midway Island in Pacific Ocean, and black coral from Hawaii. The world–famous *akabar* variety of black coral, up to 3 m long and 25 cm in diameter, comes from the Red Sea and the Indian Ocean, near Sokotra Island and Mauritius. It also occurs off the shores of China and Cuba. Blue coral (*akosi*), probably the rarest variety, has been found in the Atlantic Ocean near the Cameroon coast, with another occurrence described from Funafiti Atoll in the Pacific Ocean. Yellow–brown coral comes from the Aleutian Islands and near Alaska in the northern Pacific Ocean.

*Different–colored corals from various localities,
Southeast Asia..*

Processing: cabochons, balls, beads,
drilled pieces, carvings, engravings, and
small lapidary objects; also used in natural shape
Similar minerals: none

Imitations: porcelain, celluloid, plastic,
glass, recently also pressed corals (made
of coral splinters)
Identification: hardness
Care: Protect coral from abrasion, also from
heat, perspiration, and cosmetics, which
cause it to pale and age. Color can be restored by immersing stone in hydrogen peroxide for a short time. Clean in soap and
water only; do not use steam cleaning.

Platinum

Pt

From Spanish *plata* – "silver," for which it was first mistaken

Color: silver white, steel gray • **Diaphaneity:** opaque • **Luster:** metallic • **Fracture:** hackly • **Cleavage:** none • **Hardness:** 4–4.5 • **Streak:** steel gray, silver white • **Specific gravity:** 14–19 (pure 21.5) • **Refractive index:** none • **Birefringence:** none • **Dispersion:** none • **Pleochroism:** none • **Luminescence:** none • **Chemistry:** trace amounts of Fe, Ir, Os, Pd, Rh, Ni, Ru, Cu, Au • **Special features:** malleability, electric conductivity • **Treatment:** changes properties with addition of other metals

History: Discovered in the tombs of 12th–dynasty Egyptian pharaohs (2000 B.C.), platinum was also known to Mesoamerican Indians. Platinum coins were minted in Russia as recently as 1828–1844. Although originally not assigned a high value, platinum is today one of the most valuable of precious metals.

Chakra: forehead

Healing effects: strengthens deliberative powers; relieves headaches, earaches; discharge stone in lukewarm water, then recharge briefly in sunlight

Host rocks: ultrabasic rocks, placers

Occurrences: A rare mineral, platinum occurs in only a few localities. Small deposits have been found in Alaska and Nevada, with larger nuggets coming from California (Trinity River). Platinum is known from Canada (Ontario), Colombia, and Ecuador, with lesser occurrences in Brazil, Australia, New Zealand, and Indonesia (Borneo and Sumatra). Economically important deposits are located in Ethiopia (Jubdo) and South Africa, where platinum is mined at the Bushveld complex, which extends into Zimbabwe, and also in Burundi. Platinum mining in Russia dates back to 1825 (Ural Mts., vicinity of Nizhni Tagil). Recently, the Siberian deposit at Norilsk has become much more important. Less important deposits occur also in Finland, France, and Portugal. Platinum is usually found in small nuggets. Larger nuggets, up to 10 kg (Nevjansk, Ural Mts.), are very rare. The biggest nugget discovered to date was found there in 1912 and

Platinum nugget, 50 mm wide, 84.80 g, Nizhni Tagil, Russia.

Platinum crystal intergrowth, 4 mm wide, Konder, Ayano–Maiskii Region, Russia.

weighed 16 kg. Rare platinum crystals from Konder in Russia have recently appeared on the market.

Processing: used in jewelry industry at fineness 950/1,000, with Pd, Os, and Ir added

Similar minerals: silver

Imitations: other metals

Identification: specific gravity, hardness

Care: Protect platinum from abrasion. Clean with jeweler's polish.

Gold

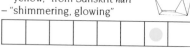

Au
Akin to Old English *geolu*
– "yellow," from Sanskrit *hari*
– "shimmering, glowing"

History: Gold has been known as a precious metal since the 4th millennium B.C. It was prized by the Sumerians, ancient Egyp-

Color: golden yellow, yellow–white • **Diaphaneity:** opaque, translucent in very thin layers (blue–green tint) • **Luster:** metallic • **Fracture:** hackly • **Cleavage:** none • **Hardness:** 2.5–3, malleable • **Streak:** yellow, lustrous • **Specific gravity:** 19.28 • **Refractive index:** none • **Birefringence:** none • **Dispersion:** none • **Pleochroism:** none • **Luminescence:** none • **Chemistry:** trace amounts of Ag, Hg, Cu, Pd, Rh • **Special features:** high malleability, electric conductivity • **Treatment:** changes properties with addition of other elements

Platy gold, 62 mm high, Tuolumne Co., California.

tians, Aztecs, Incas, Mayans, Greeks, and Romans, who used it first as a cult object and later as money. Ancient Egyptian coins called ducats, each weighing 14 g, were minted from gold alloy. The first Lydian coins (7th century B.C.) were made of a gold–silver (73:27) alloy and also weighed 14 g, while the aureus coins of ancient Rome weighed 4.5–8.2 g. A universal symbol of wealth and power, gold remains a monetary standard to this day. Its uses have extended to several modern technologies, in particular, electronics and optics.

Chakra: navel

Healing effects: slows aging; relieves depression; discharge stone in lukewarm water, then recharge briefly in sunlight

Host rocks: hydrothermal deposits, placers, cementation zones

Occurrences: Gold is known from all over the world. Ancient mines in India (Kolar region), in operation for centuries, have reached a depth of 3,000 m (9,800 ft). Important deposits also occur in Japan (vicinity of Oguchi and Kágoshima), the Philippines (Luzon), New Guinea (Bulolo River), Fiji, and New Zealand. Huge nuggets (68.26 kg – 1857; 71.03 kg – 1869; 92.0 kg – 1872) have been discovered in Australia, a significant gold producer, with extensive deposits in South Australia (Olympic Dam), Western Australia (Kalgoorlie), Victoria (old placers), and Queensland (nuggets). Discovered in Colorado (Cripple

Creek), California (35 kg nugget – near Sacramento), Nevada (Carlin), Alaska (Klondike), and South Dakota (Homestake Mine in the Black Hills), gold has played a crucial role in U.S. history. It also occurs in many Canadian localities (Yukon, Northwest Territories, and almost all provinces), with famous deposits in Ontario (Porcupine, Kirkland Lake, Hemle, and Timmins) and Quebec (Bousquet, Doyon, Val d'Or). Gold is mined in Mexico (El Bargueno), San Salvador, the Dominican Republic, Chile (El Indio), Peru, Colombia, Brazil. A nugget weighing 153 kg is reported from Chile, and another, weighing 62.3 kg, from Brazil. Almost all the countries of Africa have produced some gold. Historically, the most important mines were in Egypt (mined in Nubia by the pharaohs). Although important deposits occur in Ghana (Ashanti region) and Zimbabwe, the world's largest producer is South Africa, where the gold–bearing conglomerates of the Witwatersrand region have yielded 700 to 1,000 tons of gold per year for over a century. The South Africa's

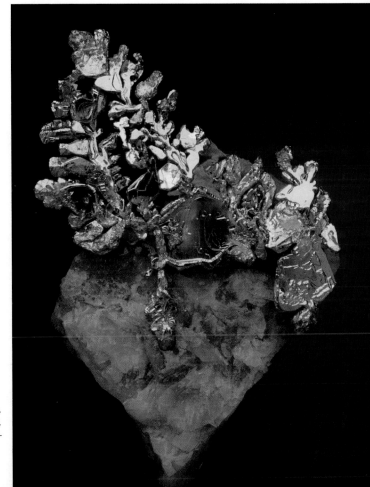

Gold, 56 mm high, Eagle's Nest Mine, Placer Co., California.

Gold earrings with pearls, by Karel Valter, Geneva.

in the Ural Mts. (Berezovsk, Miass, Nizhni Tagil). A nugget weighing 36.04 kg was found near Miass in 1842, and two weighing 14.2 and 9.4 kg in 1936. Mining is currently concentrated in Siberia (Kolyma River basin, Aldan). Important gold production also comes from Uzbekistan (Kochbulakh). Gold occurs in Germany (Brandholz, Goldkronach, Isar and Eder River sediments), and many historically important deposits are known from the Czech Republic (Jílové, Kasejovice, Křepice, Zlaté Hory) and from Slovakia (Kremnica – for more than 1,000 years; also Magurka). Europe's principal gold mines are located in Romania, in the "Golden Quadrangle" between Brad, Baia de Aries, Sacarimb, and Rosia Montana, with other deposits in France, Sweden, and Finland.

Carltonville Mine is the deepest in the world (3,840 m or 11,500 ft, as of 1975). In Russia, another of the world's largest producers, gold has historically been mined

Gold, 34 mm wide, Irish Creek, Grass Valley, California.

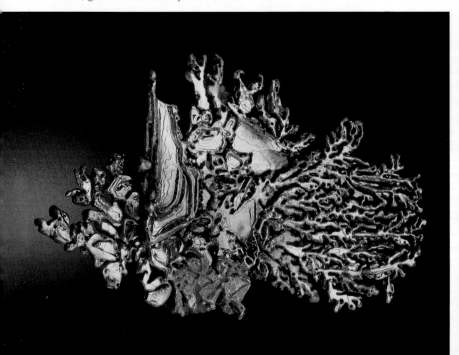

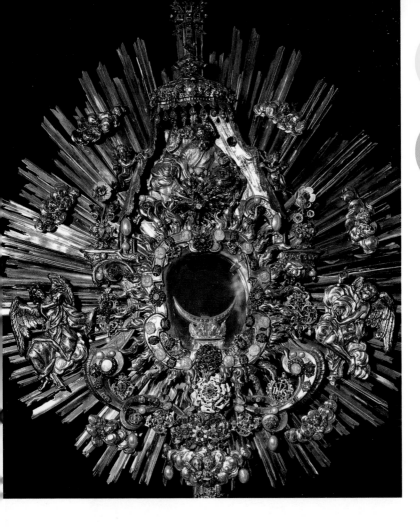

"Ring Monstrance" from the Loreta treasury, Prague, adorned with 492 diamonds and 186 rubies, sapphires, pearls, emeralds, amethysts, and almandines. Made in Prague in 1748.

Processing: Used in jewelry, decorative objects, gilding. Because gold is soft, it is often alloyed with Cu or Ag (**red gold**), sometimes with Ni or Pd (**white gold**). Gold content is expressed in 1/1,000s (pure gold is 1,000/1,000). The term *karat* (= 1/24) is also used (pure gold is 24 kt.), as opposed to *carat* (1 ct. = 200 mg), the common unit of weight for gemstones. In making jewelry, the fineness most often used is 585/1,000 (14 kt.); less often 375/1,000 (9 kt.); sometimes also 750/1,000 (18 kt.).

Similar minerals: pyrite, chalcopyrite

Imitations: brass

Identification: hardness, streak, chemical methods

Care: Protect gold from abrasion. Clean with jeweler's polish.

Silver

Ag

From Old English *seolfor* – "silver," ultimately from Akkadian *sarapu* – "to refine or smelt"

History: One of the oldest known precious metals, silver has historically been used as money. Today it is also an important element in photography, electronics, and medicine. Although it was fairly rare in the tombs of Egyptian pharaohs, nice silver objects are known from Chaldean tombs (4th millennium B.C.). At one time quite popular in Persia, silver was mined by the ancient Greeks, Spaniards, Phoenicians, Carthaginians, and Romans. Great healing powers were attributed to "silver water," later found to have bactericidal properties.

Chakra: base

Color: silver white, which tarnishes and blackens • **Diaphaneity:** opaque • **Luster:** metallic, dull • **Fracture:** hackly • **Cleavage:** none • **Hardness:** 2.5–3, malleable • **Streak:** white, lustrous • **Specific gravity:** 9.2–12.0 • **Refractive index:** none • **Birefringence:** none • **Dispersion:** none • **Pleochroism:** none • **Luminescence:** none • **Chemistry:** trace amounts of Au, Hg, Bi, Sb, Cu, As • **Special features:** malleability, electric conductivity • **Treatment:** changes properties with addition of other elements

Healing effects: slows aging; calms emotions; relieves depression; discharge stone in lukewarm water, then recharge briefly in sunlight

Host rocks: volcanic rocks, low– and medium–temperature veins, hydrothermal deposits

Occurrences: Many deposits have been found in the United States and Canada –

Silver, 74 mm high, Batopilas, Mexico.

Silver, 103 mm high, Kongsberg, Norway.

in Arizona (silver masses up to 1.35 t or 1.5 short tons), Nevada, Michigan, Alaska, and in Ontario, British Columbia, Northwest Territories (Great Bear Lake area). Mexico has been a very important producer since the 16th century, with famous deposits in Guanajuato, El Oro, and Batopilas. It is mined in Chile, Bolivia, and Peru, where the best–known deposit is in Cerro de Pasco, mined since the 17th century. Other important occurrences are in Australia, Japan, Russia (Altai Mts.), and Kazakhstan. Prior to the discovery of America, European silver deposits were very important. Famous localities include Schneeberg (silver wires up to 40 cm long), Freiberg, Mansfeld, St. Andreasberg, and Wittichen in Germany; Jihlava, Kutná Hora, Jáchymov, Příbram in the Czech Republic; Banská Štiavnica in Slovakia; and Kongsberg (silver blocks up to 100 kg) in Norway. It was also mined in Sweden (Sala) and France (Sainte–Marie–aux–Mines).

Processing: used in jewelry, decorative objects, small utility goods, silver plating; often alloyed with Cu and Au

Similar minerals: platinum

Imitations: other metals

Identification: specific gravity, hardness

Care: Protect silver from abrasion. Clean with jeweler's polish.

Tektites

Natural silica glass (75%)

From Greek *tektos* – "melted"

6

History: Known since Paleolithic times, tektites were first used to make tools, and later as amulets.

Astrology: birthstone for Gemini

Chakra: heart

Healing effects: energizes; revitalizes; discharge stone in lukewarm water, then recharge briefly in sunlight

Source: meteor impacts with Earth's surface (tektites are considered natural glasses)

Occurrences: Although relatively common, tektites are for the most part confined to their strewn fields. The most famous specimens were discovered in 1788 in the Vltava River basin (Moldau in German, hence **moldavites**) and western Moravia,

Different–colored cut tektites; largest, 45 ct., is from Radomilice, Czech Republic. Libyan glass from Egypt is in center of lower row.

Color: green, brown–green, black––green, olive green, black; sometimes yellow, white; rarely multicolored • **Diaphaneity:** transparent to opaque • **Luster:** glassy • **Fracture:** conchoidal • **Cleavage:** none • **Hardness:** 5.5–6.5, brittle • **Streak:** white • **Specific gravity:** 2.21–2.96 • **Refractive index:** N–1.470–1.540 • **Birefringence:** none • **Dispersion:** none • **Pleochroism:** none • **Luminescence:** none • **Chemistry:** trace amounts of Al, Fe, Ca, Na, K, Mg, Ti • **Special features:** distinct fluid texture, craterlike surface pitting, fluid and gaseous inclusions • **Treatment:** surface often etched in dilute acids

present–day Czech Republic. Moldavites from these two strewn fields, although differing in shape, size, color hues, and surface texture, are all presumed to originate in the Riess impact crater in Germany. The average weight of southern Bohemian moldavites, found in Upper Miocene and younger sediments, is about 8 g, but a few remarkable pieces weigh over 90 g (110.9 g from Strpí, 96.8 g from Veselí nad Lužnicí, 93.9 g from Habří). Well–known localities are Besednice,

Assorted typical shapes of moldavites from southern Bohemia; largest, 56 mm long, comes from Dobrkovská Lhotka, Czech Republic.

Ločenice, Habří, Kamenný Újezd, and Slavče. Darker, less transparent, with less evolved surface texture, Moravian moldavites are also much larger (258.5 g from Slavice, 235 g from Terůvky, 232.5 g from Štěpánovice). The best-known Moravian localities are Kojatice, Slavice, Štěpánovice, Slavětice, Mohelno, and Dukovany. Rare, redeposited moldavites have been found in Germany (near Dresden) and Austria. Black-green tektites (up to 3 kg) with less evolved surface texture are known from Vietnam, Cambodia, Thailand, and Laos (**indochinites**). Tektites have also been found in Malaysia, on Sumatra, Banak, and Billiton Islands (**billitonites**); in the Philippines (**philippinites** or **rizalites**); on Java (black **javanites**); and in Kazakhstan (rare **irghizites**). **Australites** come from Australia; **Darwin glass**, which is lighter and suitable for faceting, from Tasmania. Two strewn fields have been discovered in the United States – in Texas (black **bediasites**) and in Georgia (dark green **georgianites**). Tektites are also mentioned from Peru and Colombia. **Ivorites**

are known from the Ivory Coast. Tektites from Egypt and Libya, referred to as "**Libyan glass**," are light yellow to yellow-green, weigh up to 5 kg, and are suitable for faceting.

Processing: faceted cuts, cabochons, carvings; also used in natural shape

Similar minerals: obsidian, verdelite

Imitations: glass, slags

Identification: hardness, specific gravity, optical methods

Care: Protect tektites from heat, sudden temperature changes, and sudden shocks. Clean in soap and water. Ultrasonic cleaning is also recommended. Do not use steam cleaning.

Cut moldavite with air bubble, 33.35 ct., Radomilice, Czech Republic.

Obsidian

(volcanic glass)

After Obsius, Roman who first brought it to Rome from Ethiopia

History: Obsidian was used to make scrapers, knives, and arrowheads in Paleolithic and Neolithic times, and later as a decorative stone. The oldest finds date back about 9,000 years (Mesopotamia).
Astrology: birthstone for Scorpio
Chakra: base
Healing effects: sharpens mental acuity; discharge stone in lukewarm water, then recharge briefly in sunlight

Color: black, gray, black–brown, bluish, greenish; sometimes with silver or golden reflections, white cristobalite crystals (***snowflake obsidian***), or iridescent colors • **Diaphaneity:** translucent, opaque • **Luster:** glassy • **Fracture:** conchoidal • **Cleavage:** none • **Hardness:** 5–6, very brittle • **Streak:** white • **Specific gravity:** 2.3–3.0 • **Refractive index:** N–1.48–1.51 • **Birefringence:** none • **Dispersion:** 0.010 • **Pleochroism:** none • **Luminescence:** none • **Chemistry:** trace amounts of other elements, inclusions of other minerals, fluid inclusions • **Special features:** iridescence, chatoyancy • **Treatment:** not known

Host rocks: volcanic rocks
Occurrences: Common in volcanic regions, obsidian of high quality has been mined in the United States. The best–known localities are in Utah (snowflake obsidian), Arizona, New Mexico ("***Apache tears***"), Oregon (iridescent from Glass Butte), California, Wyoming, and Hawaii (***tachylite***–basalt glass). Different varieties of Mexican obsidian have been mined in Sierra de los Navayas (Hidalgo), Jalisco, and Querétaro. Other obsidian deposits

Snowflake obsidian, United States.

Obsidian, Armenia.

Obsidian, step cut with air bubbles, 59 ct., Armenia.

Obsidian arrowheads, 75 mm long, Mexico. Obsidian cuts, "Apache tears," 10 ct., Arizona.

are located in Guatemala, Nicaragua, and Ecuador. African obsidian comes mainly from Ethiopia. Asian obsidian has been found in Japan, Armenia, and Russia (Kamchatka, Transbaikalia), and European obsidian, in Slovakia (Zemplín), Hungary (Palházy region), Italy (Lipari Islands), and Iceland.

Processing: faceted cuts, cabochons, carvings, table cuts
Similar minerals: tektites
Imitations: glass
Identification: physical and microscopic features
Care: Protect obsidian from heat and sudden shocks. Clean in soap and cold water. Do not use steam cleaning.

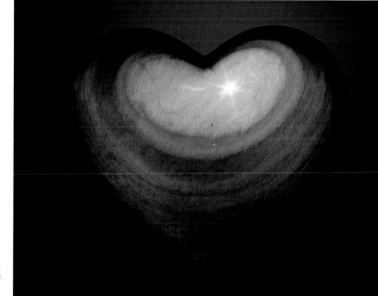

Rainbow obsidian
90 mm wide, Mexico.

Rocks

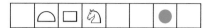

History: Originally used to make tools and weapons, rocks were later used to make lapidary, decorative, and utility objects as well as jewelry. Many different kinds of rocks have enjoyed varying periods of popularity through the ages. Diorite porphyrite was used by the Egyptians and Romans; gabbro porphyrites, by the Greeks. Various sedimentary rocks (especially limestones) have had widespread use, while quartzites, hornfelses, and other metamorphic rocks have been used locally.

Origin: Igneous rocks (granites, granodiorites, diorites, syenites, gabbros, dolerites, norites, dunites, serpentinites) crystallize directly from magma; extrusive rocks (rhyolites, trachytes, dacites, andesites, basalts) belong to this same group. Metamorphic rocks (slates, phyllites, mica schists, gneisses, migmatites, amphibolites, marbles, hornfelses, skarns, eclogites) are metamorphosed igneous or sedimentary rocks.

Sedimentary rocks (conglomerates, sandstones, clays, limestones, travertines, arcoses, graywackes, marls) are formed by the sedimentation of fine particles.

Color: various hues of gray, red, brown, black, beige, pink, and green, depending on mineral composition. Basic and ultrabasic rocks are generally green to green–black; acid rocks are lighter, gray–white, pinkish, often with phenocrysts of rock–forming minerals; metamorphic rocks are usually gray–green to dark green, while sedimentary rocks are often yellow to yellow–brown. • **Diaphaneity:** opaque • **Luster:** mostly dull • **Fracture:** uneven, smooth, splintery • **Cleavage:** none; only fissility along foliation or fractures • **Hardness:** highly variable, depending on mineral composition; clay and claystones, 1–2; eclogites and other metamorphic rocks, 6–7

Occurrences: Rocks used in making jewelry, lapidary and decorative objects can be found the world over. Alkaline syenites for decorative objects come from Greenland and Russia (Kola Peninsula). Amazonite granites have been mined in Mongolia, Libya, the United States, and Canada. Aplites and pegmatites (especially graphic and amazonite pegmatites) are

Granite, Liberec, Czech Republic.

Graphic pegmatite, Dolní Bory, Czech Republic.

Limestone with fossils, China.

Marble, Italy.

known from Russia, Ukraine, Norway, and the United States. Unakite is known from Greenland and South Africa. Iridescent orthoamphibolites are known from Wyoming. Rummites come from Greenland. Most widely used among metamorphic rocks, marble is quarried in Italy (Carrara), Greece, Germany, Belgium, France, the Czech Republic, the United States, Cuba, Algeria, and Morocco. Ophicalcites, similar to marble, are known from Greece, Russia, and Italy; other metamorphic rocks, such as jaspilite and porcellanite from Russia and the Czech Republic, are less widely used.

Processing: plates, cabochons, small lapidary and utility objects

"Ruin marble," Italy.

Porcellanite, Komňa, Czech Republic.

Wollastonite skarn, Dalnegorsk, Russia.

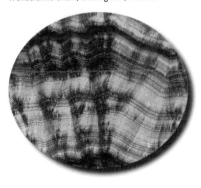

184

Abbreviations used in gemstone classification

Clarity

IF
flawless even under
10x magnifying loupe

VVS
flaws visible with some
difficulty under loupe

P1
many flaws and inclusions,
barely visible to naked eye
looking from above

VS
flaws visible
only under loupe

P2
many flaws and inclusions,
visible to naked eye and
limiting brilliance of the stone

SI
small inclusions
and flaws, identifiable
using loupe

P3
dense groupings of inclusions
and flaws, significantly influenc-
ing brilliance of the stone

Color

B blue	**YG** yellow-green	**RP** red-purple
BG blue-green	**Y** yellow	**PR** purple-red
GB green-blue	**YR** yellow-red	**P** purple
G green	**RY** red-yellow	**PB** purple-blue
GY green yellow	**R** red	**BP** blue-purple

Color intensity

VP very pale	**ML** medium light	**MD** medium dark	**VD** very dark
P pale	**M** medium	**D** dark	**O** opaque

Quality of cut

A very good	**B** good	**C** average	**D** poor

Actual size (diameter) and weight of brilliant cut diamonds

2.58 mm	3.25 mm	4.10 mm	5.15 mm	6.50 mm	7.50 mm	8.20 mm	9.35 mm
0.10 ct	0.20 ct	0.25 ct	0.50 ct	1.00 ct	1.50 ct	2.00 ct	3.00 ct

Rare gemstones

The mineral species described in this book are principal, important, or common gemstones. Other minerals, often only locally important, are sometimes used as gemstones. With the growing number of gem collectors, more and more minerals are cut today, most of them rare, even though they are either too soft or too fragile to be set in jewelry. Some are very rare (only a few pieces known); others yield only a negligible percentage of gem rough suitable for cutting. Dealing with their particular properties (heat sensitivity, perfect cleavage, brittleness) often requires very special and sophisticated cutting techniques. A list of rare gemstones is given on the following page.

Rare gemstones by hardness in descending order

taafeite
painite
hambergite
grandidierite
dumortierite
sapphirine
cassiterite
boracite
jeremejevite
vesuvianite
cyprine
tephroite
zoisite
clinozoisite
prehnite
sillimanite
tantalite
chondrodite
clinohumite
millarite
petalite
aegirine
diaspore
hyalophane
pollucite
helvite
periclase
sinhalite
rutile
dioptase
titanite
enstatite
bronzite
hypersthene

tremolite
actinolite
smaragdite
noseane
hauyne
nepheline
cancrinite
datolite
eudialyte
hemimorphite
willemite
natrolite
pectolite
ekanite
stibiotantalite
scorzalite
beryllonite
herderite
durangite
anatase
brookite
goethite
psilomelane
magnetite
nickeline
nickeline
wollastonite
tugtupite
apophyllite
libethenite
pseudomalachite
purpurite
scheelite
colemanite

magnesite
siderite
zincite
shattuckite
chrysotile
howlite
euchroite
adamite
mimetite
vanadinite
pyromorphite
scorodite
wulfenite
celestine
anhydrite
barite
anglesite
witherite
dolomite
cerussite
sepiolite
fuchsite
kaemmererite
lepidolite
vivianite
crocoite
proustite
talc
selenite
stichtite
graphite
sulfur
jet

Synthetic and imitation gemstones

Synthetic gemstones can be divided into stones that are chemical equivalents of natural gemstones (synthetic diamonds, periclases, corundums, spinels, rutiles, cassiterites, scheelites, quartzes, opals, alexandrites, emeralds, zircons, spodumenes, malachites, turquoises, and coral) and stones with no natural equivalents (fianite, yttrium oxide, YAG, galiant, yttrium aluminate, fabulite, lithium niobate, and lithium tantalate).
Imitation gemstones, which are neither chemical equivalents of the stones they imitate nor artificial stones in their own right, can be made from glass, bakelite, polyamide, celluloid, perspex, polystyrene, various glazings, and other materials.

Recommended reading

Anderson, B. W. 1980. *Gem Testing*. London: Butterworth.

Arem, J. E. 1987. *Color Encyclopedia of Gemstones*. New York: Van Nostrand Reinhold.

Arem, J. E. 1992. *Gems and Jewelry*. Tucson, AZ: Geoscience Press.

Bancroft, P. 1984. *Gem and Crystal Treasures*. Fallbrook, CA: Western Enterprises.

Bank, H. 1971. *Auf der Welt der Edelsteine*. Frankfurt-am-Main: Umschauverlag.

Bauer, J. 1974. *Minerals, Rocks and Precious Stones*. Prague: Artia.

Bauer, J., and Bouška V., 1983. *Precious and Semiprecious Stones*. Prague: Artia.

Bauer, M. 1904. *Precious Stones*. Trans. L. Spencer. 2 vols. Reprint, New York: Dover, 1968. (Original title: *Edelsteinkunde*; first published in 1896.)

Chocron, D. S. *Healing with Crystals and Gemstones*. York Beach, ME: Samuel Weiser.

Ďuďa, R., and Rejl, L. 1986. *Minerals of the World*. Prague: Artia.

Hall, C. 1994. *Eyewitness Handbook of Gemstones*. London: Dorling Kindersley.

Hurlbut, C. S., and Kammerling, R. C. 1991. *Gemology*. 2d ed. New York: Wiley.

Kunz, G. F. 1968. *Gems and Precious Stones of North America*. New York: Dover.

Liddicoat, R. T., Jr. 1989. *Handbook of Gem Identification*. 12th ed. Carlsbad, CA: Gemological Institute of America.

Raphaell, K. 1987. *Crystal Healing*. Santa Fe, NM: Aurora Press.

Schumann, W. 1977. *Gemstones of the World*. New York: Sterling.

Sinkankas, J. 1972. *Gemstones and Mineral Data Book*. Tucson, AZ: Geoscience Press.

Sinkankas, J., 1989. *Gem Cutting: A Lapidary's Manual*. New York: Van Nostrand Reinhold.

Sinkankas, J., 1997. *Gemstones of North America*. Vol. 3. Tucson, AZ: Geoscience Press.

Smith, G. F. H. 1972. *Gemstones*. London: Chapman and Hall.

Van Landingham, S. L. 1985. *Geology of World Gem Deposits*. New York: Van Nostrand Reinhold.

Webster R., 1979. *A Gemologist's Compendium*. New York: Van Nostrand Reinhold.

Webster R., 1983. *Gems: Their Sources, Description and Identifications*. 4th ed. London: Butterworth

Journals

Gems and Gemology, Carlsbad, CA

Lapidary Journal, Devon, PA

Lapis, Munich, Germany

Minerál, Brno, Czech Republic

Mineralien Welt, Haltern, Germany

Mineralogical Record, Tucson, AZ

Index

About the Authors

RUDOLF ĎUĎA is a native Slovakian with a doctorate in the field of mineralogy from Komenský University, Bratislava. Currently, he is a mineralogist at the East Slovak Museum, Košice. His main focus is on precious stones. Along with his many book projects, he is the author of over 100 articles on mineralogy published in Slovakia and abroad.

LUBOŠ REJL grew up in the Czech Republic, where his love of mineralogy led to a doctorate in the field of natural history from Masaryk university, Brno. Employed as a geologist, much of his research has been about the minerals and gemstones of the Bohemian Massif and the Carpathian Mts. He is Editor–in Chief of the periodical, Mineral, which is published in the Czech and Slovak Republics. Many of Rejl's books about mineralogy and gemstones have been written in collaboration with Rudolf Ďuďa.

Gem and Mineral Classics
from Geoscience Press

GEMSTONES OF AFGHANISTAN by Gary W. Bowersox and Bonita E. Chamberlain. A superbly illustrated survey of the gems of Afghanistan, their locations, and their impact on that nation's economy and society.
$60.00, *hardcover, 240 pages, 100 illustrations (40 in color)*, ISBN 0–945005–19–9.

GEMSTONES OF EAST AFRICA by Peter C. Keller. The comprehensive chronicle of the richest gemstone deposits in the world, replete with maps and superb color photographs.
$50.00, *hardcover, 160 pages, 70 illustrations*, ISBN 0–945005–08–3.

GEMSTONES OF NORTH AMERICA, VOLUME III by John Sinkankas. The final volume of this resource provides all new information about gemstone exploration and development after Volume II was published in 1976.
$65.00, *hardcover, 544 pages, 17 color and 67 b/w photographs*, ISBN 0–945005–22–9.

GEMS AND JEWELRY by Joel E. Arem. This pocket–sized classic guide to precious stones and their settings will teach anyone how to shop for gems with confidence.
$12.00, *paperback, 178 pages, 186 color photographs*, ISBN 0–945005–09–1.

THE AMBER BOOK by Ake Dahlstrom and Leif Brost. Written in an entertaining, non–technical style, this book explores the origin of amber, its folklore, how to detect fakes, and its uses in lapidary.
$27.00, *hardcover, 134 pages, 80 color and 24 b/w photographs*, ISBN 0–945005–23–7.

Please ask your bookstore to order any of these books for you or you may order directly from Geoscience Press, Inc. PO BOX 42948, Tucson, AZ 85733–2948; voice: 520–326–9595; fax: 520–326–8684.

GEOSCIENCE
PRESS, Inc.
Tucson, Arizona

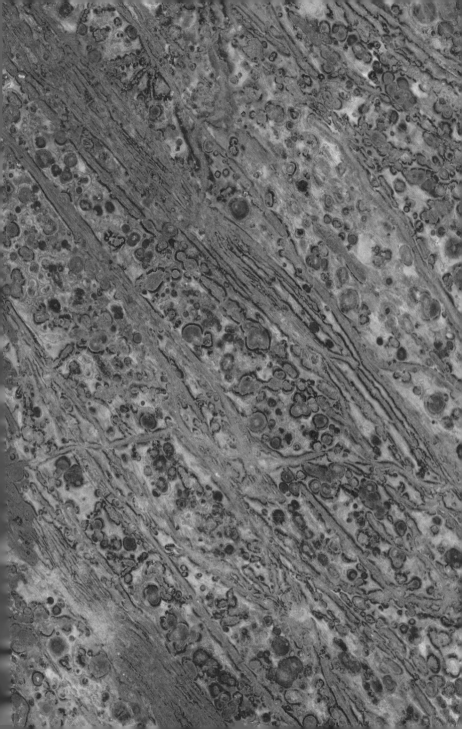